The Versatile Op Amp

The Versatile Op Amp

Michael Kahn
New York City Community College

HOLT, RINEHART AND WINSTON, INC.

*New York   Chicago   San Francisco   Atlanta   Dallas
Montreal   Toronto   London   Sydney*

Preface

The electronics field is changing rapidly. With the trend toward micro-miniaturization, the day of the discrete component circuit designer is drawing to a close. The time is approaching when the electronics field will diverge in two major directions: In a sense, the circuit designer will become a physicist; that is, he will be concerned primarily with the fabrication of integrated circuits. The second type of engineer will become a mathematician. His function will be the interconnection of the various integrated circuit blocks to synthesize a complete system.

This text has been prepared to meet the demands of the future. It concentrates on an extremely versatile device known as the modern op amp. Unlike the traditional discrete component amplifier, the op amp is manufactured and purchased as a *single* package. Due to its monolithic nature, the op amp lends itself to a relatively simple and direct means of analysis. It is because of this fact that the text deals with an entirely new analytical philosophy.

This text has been written for students in a junior college or technical institute. It is necessary that the student be familiar with intermediate algebra and trigonometry as well as the fundamentals of dc and ac circuit analysis. Since the basic elements of amplification, feedback, dc offset and

v

drift, frequency response, and phase compensation are covered, the text can stand by itself. It can be used for an entire electronics course, a portion of the course, or for a special course in op amps.

The first chapter is an introduction to amplifiers. It also lists the many advantages of single-package amplifiers over discrete ones. Chapter 2 deals with the black box concept. Throughout the text, the emphasis is on the treatment of the op amp as a black box, rather than as a multistage amplifier. The text concentrates on an analytical approach as opposed to one stressing fabrication techniques. In other words, it is directed at the op amp *user*. Chapter 3 discusses the practical op amp. Chapter 4 is concerned with the incorporation of negative feedback to stabilize the gain in a noninverting amplifier, while Chapter 5 does the same for an inverting amplifier. In Chapter 6, an examination is made of the effects of offset and drift on the dc operation of the amplifier. Chapter 7 handles the concept of frequency response, while Chapter 8 deals with the phase compensation methods which are employed to prevent oscillations. Finally, Chapter 9 discusses some of the many applications of the op amp.

I wish to express my sincere thanks to the entire staff of the Electrical Technology Department of the New York City Community College, without whose suggestions and encouragement this text would not have been possible.

Brooklyn, New York   MICHAEL KAHN
February 1970

Contents

Preface, v

Chapter 1   The Amplifier,   2

1-1 The Characteristic Curve, 1
1-2 The Diode, 5
1-3 The Load Line, 7
1-4 The Three-Terminal Device, 11
1-5 The Amplifier, 16
1-6 The Modern Op Amp, 23

Chapter 2   The Black Box,   31

2-1 The Black Box, 31
2-2 The Z-Parameters, 33
2-3 Applications of the Black Box, 38

Chapter 3   The Practical Op Amp,   43

3-1 The Op Amp Package, 43
3-2 The Black Box Equivalent, 48

3-3   The Common-Mode Rejection Ratio, 57
3-4   Single-Input Applications, 60

Chapter   4   The Noninverting Amplifier,   66

4-1   Gain Variation, 67
4-2   Negative Feedback, 68
4-3   The Closed Loop Gain, 73
4-4   The Feedback Amplifier, 82
4-5   The Voltage Follower, 87

Chapter   5   The Inverting Amplifier,   92

5-1   The Feedback Mechanism, 92
5-2   The Miller Effect, 95
5-3   The Closed Loop Gain, 99
5-4   The Feedback Amplifier, 103
5-5   The Buffer Amplifier, 104
5-6   The Differential Amplifier, 109

Chapter   6   dc Offset and Drift,   114

6-1   The Offset Voltage, 115
6-2   Offset Voltage Compensation, 119
6-3   Drift, 124
6-4   The Offset Current, 127
6-5   The Error Voltage, 131
6-6   The Error Voltage Referred to the Input, 139
6-7   Drift in ac Amplifiers, 142
6-8   Drift in the Noninverting Amplifier, 144

Chapter   7   Frequency Response,   148

7-1   The High-Frequency Equivalent Circuit, 148
7-2   The Decibel, 152
7-3   The Frequency Response Curve, 154
7-4   The Significance of Frequency Response, 161
7-5   The Closed Loop Frequency Response, 166
7-6   The Slew Rate, 173

Chapter   8   Oscillation and Phase Compensation,   179

8-1   Oscillations, 179
8-2   Stability Criteria, 182

8-3   A Compensation Network, 192
8-4   Phase Compensation, 196
8-5   A Practical Network, 201

Chapter 9   Applications,   207

9-1   The ac Amplifier, 207
9-2   The Approximate Equivalent Circuit, 208
9-3   The Inverter, 211
9-4   The Adder, 212
9-5   The Averager, 213
9-6   The Scaler, 213
9-7   The Integrator, 214
9-8   The Log Amplifier, 215
9-9   The General Problem, 217

Answers to Selected Odd-Numbered Problems,   218

References,   220

List of Terms,   221

Index, 225

The Versatile Op Amp

1

The Amplifier

What is an amplifier? Why all the fuss about its importance? The amplifier is probably the most commonly used electronic circuit. It can be found in radios, television sets, radar installations, computers, control systems, and so on. It is used whenever we wish to boost the strength of an electronic signal. In this chapter, we shall begin by developing some basic techniques for handling electronic circuits; then we shall discuss the nature of an electronic amplifier. Finally, we shall present an introduction to the modern op amp, indicating the many advantages to be accrued from its use.

1-1   The Characteristic Curve

In order to pave the way for our discussion of the amplifier, we shall begin by developing a new graphical technique. Suppose we have a variable source of voltage connected to a 10 Ω resistor, as shown in Figure 1-1(a). Let us consider the voltage v_{AB} to be *positive* when the potential at terminal A is positive with respect to that at terminal B, and the current i to be *positive* when it flows from terminal A to terminal B, as shown in Figure 1-1(a). Obviously, the value of i will vary as the value of the dc source

1

voltage is varied; for example, if $v_{AB} = +10$ V, $i = +1$ A, and if $v_{AB} = +20$ V, $i = +2$ A, and so on. The values of i are indicated in Table 1-1 for values of v_{AB} equal to 0 V, $+10$ V, $+20$ V, and $+30$ V.

TABLE   1-1

VALUES OF

v_{AB} AND i

v_{AB} (volts)	i (amps)
0	0
+10	+1
+20	+2
+30	+3
−10	−1
−20	−2
−30	−3

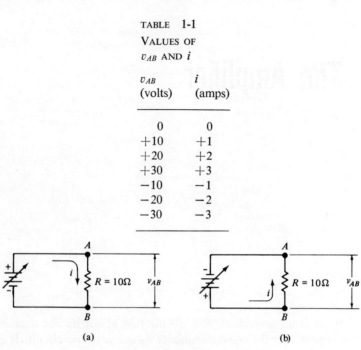

(a)   (b)

Figure 1-1

Resistive Circuit

Figure 1-1(b) shows the situation when the terminals of the source are reversed. Note that v_{AB} is now *negative*, since the potential at terminal A is negative with respect to that at terminal B. Note also that i is *negative*, since it now flows from terminal B to terminal A. The values of i are indicated in Table 1-1 for values of v_{AB} equal to -10 V, -20 V, and -30 V.

Now suppose we construct two perpendicular axes, as shown in Figure 1-2. We label the vertical axis "i" and the horizontal axis "v_{AB}." Notice in Table 1-1 that each set of values of v_{AB} and i constitutes a pair of coordinates (v_{AB}, i) which can be plotted as a point on the axes of Figure 1-2. If these points are plotted, the resulting curve is a *straight line* passing through the origin, as shown. What does this mean? It merely says that the current, i, through the 10 Ω resistor is directly proportional to the voltage, v_{AB}, across it. This is nothing more than a graphical representation of Ohm's

law. The straight line in Figure 1-2 is called the *characteristic curve* of the
10 Ω resistor. A characteristic curve of a two-terminal device is a graph of
the current through the device versus the voltage across it.

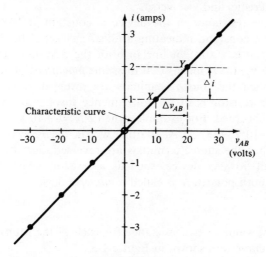

Figure 1-2

Characteristic Curve of Resistor

Since the characteristic curve of the 10 Ω resistor is a straight line, it must
have a constant slope. The slope of a straight line is equal to the vertical
distance between two points divided by the horizontal distance.

$$\text{slope} = m = \frac{\Delta i}{\Delta v_{AB}}. \tag{1-1}$$

We can select any two points. Using points X and Y in Figure 1-2, we
compute the slope of the characteristic to be

$$m = \frac{\Delta i}{\Delta v_{AB}} = \frac{1 \text{ A}}{10 \text{ V}} = \frac{1}{10} \frac{\text{A}}{\text{V}} = \frac{1}{10} \text{ mho.}$$

Note that the slope has units of *mhos*. This indicates that the slope of a
characteristic curve is a *conductance*. Remember, however, that the resistance of the device whose characteristic appears in Figure 1-2 is 10 Ω.
Therefore, we conclude that the *slope* of a characteristic curve is equal to the
conductance of the device (0.1 mho, in this case), which in turn is equal to the
reciprocal of the *resistance* (10 Ω, in this case).

$$m = G = \frac{1}{R}. \tag{1-2}$$

This is a very important point. Equation (1-2) indicates a *reciprocal* relationship between the resistance of a device and the slope of its characteristic curve. It says that the *smaller* the value of resistance, the *steeper* the slope of the characteristic, and vice versa.

Note that the resistance of the device is constant at 10 Ω. This means that the slope is constant, indicating a linear characteristic. Note also that the characteristic is a straight line in both the first and third quadrants. What does this mean? It means that the same *magnitude* of current flows in the resistor when the source terminals are reversed, indicating that the *polarity* of the resistor is of no consequence insofar as the value of its resistance is concerned. For example, when $v_{AB} = +10$ V, $i = +1$ A, and when $v_{AB} = -10$ V, $i = -1$ A. In other words, the *direction* of the current will reverse when the source terminals are reversed, but the same *amount* of current will flow. A device, such as a resistor, which has the same resistance for both polarities, is called a *bilateral* device.

EXAMPLE 1-1

Compute the value of the resistance for each of the four devices whose characteristic curves are shown in Figure 1-3.

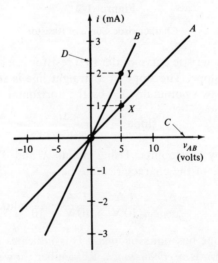

Figure 1-3

Characteristic Curves for Example 1-1

Solution

To compute the resistance of a device from its characteristic, it is not necessary to find the slope. We merely select any point on the curve and divide the voltage at that point by the current.

Curve A: Selecting point X in Figure 1-3, we find that $v_{AB} = 5$ V and $i = 1$ mA. Thus, the value of R is

$$R = \frac{v_{AB}}{i} = \frac{5 \text{ V}}{1 \text{ mA}} = 5 \text{ k}\Omega.$$

Curve B: Selecting point Y in Figure 1-3, we find that $v_{AB} = 5$ V and $i = 2$ mA. Thus, the value of R is

$$R = \frac{v_{AB}}{i} = \frac{5 \text{ V}}{2 \text{ mA}} = 2.5 \text{ k}\Omega.$$

Notice that Curve B has a steeper slope than Curve A, indicating a smaller resistance.

Curve C: Curve C is a horizontal line, and thus, it has a slope equal to zero. Since the resistance of a device is equal to the reciprocal of the slope of its characteristic, the resistance associated with Curve C is infinity. In other words, Curve C is the characteristic curve of an *open circuit*.

Curve D: Curve D is a vertical line, and thus, it has a slope equal to infinity. Therefore, the resistance associated with Curve D is zero. In other words, Curve D is the characteristic curve of a *short circuit*.

1-2 The Diode

Suppose we have a two-terminal device whose characteristic curve appears as in Figure 1-4. Notice that the characteristic is *not* a straight line passing through the origin. Thus, the device is *not* a resistor. What is it? Let us examine this characteristic in light of the material discussed in the preceding

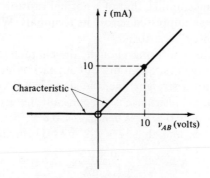

Figure 1-4

Characteristic Curve of a Diode

section. Note that the characteristic is linear in the first quadrant. In fact, we can say that when v_{AB} is positive, R is

$$R = \frac{10\ \text{V}}{10\ \text{mA}} = 1\ \text{k}\Omega.$$

In the third quadrant, however, when v_{AB} is negative, R is equal to infinity. Therefore, we conclude that this device has *two* different resistances. The resistance of the device depends upon the *polarity* of the voltage across it. Since it conducts no current when v_{AB} is negative, we call it a *unilateral* device; that is, it conducts current in *only one* direction.

The unilateral device is more commonly referred to as a *diode*. The symbol for a diode is shown in Figure 1-5(a). The arrow indicates the

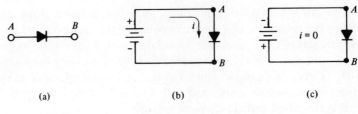

(a)   (b)   (c)

Figure 1-5

(a) Diode Symbol; (b) Forward-Biased Diode; (c) Reverse-Biased Diode

direction of current flow. When the potential at terminal A is positive with respect to that at terminal B (v_{AB} positive), we say that the diode is *forward-biased*, and current flows in the direction of the arrow, as shown in Figure 1-5(b). When the potential at terminal A is negative with respect to that at terminal B (v_{AB} negative), we say that the diode is *reverse-biased*, and the current is zero, as shown in Figure 1-5(c). In other words, we now have a device whose resistance, unlike that of a normal resistor, depends upon the polarity of the voltage impressed across its terminals. We can consider the diode to be a "one-way" resistor.

As if things are not confusing enough, the characteristic of a practical diode is *not* linear in the first quadrant, but appears as shown in Figure 1-6. Since the curve is not a straight line, the slope is not constant and if the slope is not constant, the resistance is not constant. Let us find the resistance of the diode when $v_{AB} = 0.8$ V. When $v_{AB} = 0.8$ V, the diode is biased at point X in Figure 1-6, and thus, $i = 1.2$ mA. Then, the value of R is

$$R = \frac{v_{AB}}{i} = \frac{0.8\ \text{V}}{1.2\ \text{mA}} = 670\ \Omega.$$

Therefore, when $v_{AB} = 0.8$ V, the diode behaves like a 670 Ω resistor. It acts though its characteristic curve were line OX in the figure. Now, let us find the resistance of the diode when $v_{AB} = 1.1$ V. When $v_{AB} = 1.1$ V, the diode is biased at point Y in Figure 1-6, and thus, $i = 2.6$ mA. Then, the value of R is

$$R = \frac{v_{AB}}{i} = \frac{1.1 \text{ V}}{2.6 \text{ mA}} = 420 \text{ } \Omega.$$

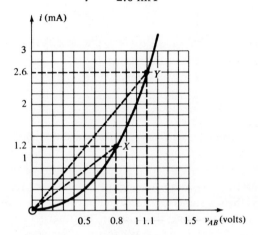

Figure 1-6

Characteristic Curve of a Diode

Therefore, when $v_{AB} = 1.1$ V, the diode behaves like a 420 Ω resistor. It acts as though its characteristic curve were line OY in the figure.

We conclude that due to its nonlinear characteristic curve, the diode is a *variable* resistor. Note that it is not a variable resistor in the same sense as a potentiometer. The resistance of a diode varies as the voltage across its terminals varies. How many different resistances does a diode have? Since the resistance is different at every point, and there are an infinite number of points, the diode has an infinite number of resistances. Thus, we do not refer to a diode as having any *one* resistance. Instead, we provide a characteristic curve that enables us to compute the resistance at any point. Now you can see the importance of the characteristic curve. We did not need it when we dealt with an ordinary resistor because its resistance is constant. However, since the resistance of a diode is *not* constant, we must have a characteristic curve in order to determine the resistance.

1-3 The Load Line

Suppose a diode is connected in series with a resistor, R_L, and a battery, V_{AA}, as shown in Figure 1-7. What is the value of the current, i? Note that the diode is connected in series with R_L. Therefore, if we knew the resistance of the diode, we could add the two resistances (the resistance of the diode and R_L) to find the total resistance, and then divide the battery voltage by this total resistance to obtain the current. Remember, however,

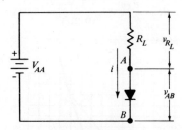

Figure 1-7

Series Circuit Containing Diode and Resistor

that the resistance of the diode depends upon the value of the current flowing through it. Therefore, we cannot compute the current through the circuit until we first find the resistance of the diode, but we cannot find the resistance of the diode until we first find the current. In other words, we cannot find the answer until we find the answer. What does this mean? The problem here is that the analytical techniques which you know are not sophisticated enough to cope with a nonlinear circuit such as the one in Figure 1-7. We must develop a new technique to help us solve this problem.

We begin by applying Kirchhoff's voltage law to the circuit of Figure 1-7:

$$V_{AA} = v_{RL} + v_{AB}, \tag{1-3}$$

$$V_{AA} = iR_L + v_{AB}. \tag{1-4}$$

Solving Equation (1-4) for i, we get

$$i = \left(-\frac{1}{R_L}\right)v_{AB} + \frac{V_{AA}}{R_L}, \tag{1-5}$$

$$y = \quad (m) \quad x \ + \ b. \tag{1-6}$$

A comparison of Equation (1-5) with Equation (1-6) indicates that Equation (1-5) is the equation of a straight line. We can plot this line if we know any two points on the line. It is most convenient to use the points at which the line intercepts the two axes. To find the v_{AB}-intercept (the point at which the line intercepts the v_{AB}-axis), we set $i = 0$ in Equation (1-5) and solve for v_{AB}:

$$i = 0 = \left(-\frac{1}{R_L}\right)v_{AB} + \frac{V_{AA}}{R_L}, \tag{1-7}$$

$$v_{AB} = V_{AA} = v_{AB}\text{-intercept}. \tag{1-8}$$

To find the i-intercept (the point at which the line intercepts the i-axis), we set $v_{AB} = 0$ in Equation (1-5) and solve for i:

$$i = \left(-\frac{1}{R_L}\right)(0) + \frac{V_{AA}}{R_L} = \frac{V_{AA}}{R_L} = i\text{-intercept.} \qquad (1\text{-}9)$$

We now have the coordinates of two points on the straight line. They are

$$(V_{AA}, 0),$$

and

$$\left(0, \frac{V_{AA}}{R_L}\right).$$

The straight line is plotted on the axes in Figure 1-8. This line is called the *load line*. The point at which the load line intersects the characteristic curve of the diode is called the *operating point*, O. This point yields infor-

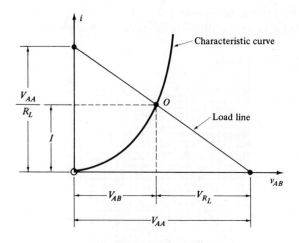

Figure 1-8

Load Line Analysis

mation concerning the values of the voltages and currents in the circuit of Figure 1-7. To determine these values, we project perpendicular (dashed) lines from the O-point to the axes, as shown in Figure 1-8. The *horizontal* distance from the origin to the O-point is labeled V_{AB}. This distance represents the actual value of the voltage across the diode in Figure 1-7. We shall use capital letters (V_{AB}) to represent *specific* voltages and currents, and small letters (v_{AB}) to represent *variables*. Notice in Figure 1-8 that the distance equal to the battery voltage, V_{AA}, minus the diode voltage, V_{AB}, is equal to the voltage drop across R_L, V_{R_L}. This is merely a consequence of Kirchhoff's voltage law. The *vertical* distance from the origin to the O-point is labeled I. This distance represents the actual value of the current in the circuit of Figure 1-7. It is important to emphasize that these graphical distances, V_{AB}, V_{R_L}, and I, represent the values of voltage and current which would be indicated by meters placed in the actual circuit.

We now have a convenient graphical technique for analyzing simple nonlinear circuits. Whenever a nonlinear device is placed in series with a resistor and a source, we can utilize the load line technique to analyze the circuit. The procedure is summarized as follows:

1.   Plot the load line.
2.   Locate the operating point.
3.   Measure the values of V_{AB}, V_{R_L}, and I.

EXAMPLE 1-2

Analyze the circuit of Figure 1-7 if $V_{AA} = 10$ V, $R_L = 2$ kΩ, and the characteristic curve of the diode is as shown in Figure 1-9.

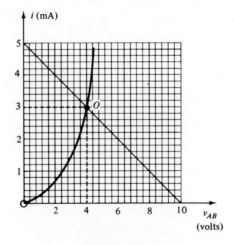

Figure 1-9

Load Line Analysis for Example 1-2

Solution

To plot the load line, we need two points. They are

$$(V_{AA}, 0) = (10 \text{ V}, 0),$$

and

$$\left(0, \frac{V_{AA}}{R_L}\right) = (0, 5 \text{ mA}).$$

The load line is shown in Figure 1-9, and the operating point is indicated. Taking measurements from the graph, we find that

$$V_{AB} = 4\text{ V} \qquad V_{RL} = 6\text{ V} \qquad I = 3\text{ mA}.$$

Notice how simple this graphical technique is. We now have enough information to compute the value of the diode resistance at the O-point.

$$R = \frac{V_{AB}}{I} = \frac{4\text{ V}}{3\text{ mA}} = 1.33\text{ k}\Omega.$$

The total resistance of the circuit is equal to the diode resistance (1.33 kΩ) plus the load resistance (2 kΩ), or 3.33 kΩ. Dividing the battery voltage (10 V) by the total resistance (3.33 kΩ), we see that $I = 3$ mA. This checks with the measurement obtained from Figure 1-9. Thus, we can say that the diode acts as a 1.33 kΩ resistor in this circuit.

1-4   The Three-Terminal Device

We are now ready for a discussion of the three-terminal device. There are a number of different types of three-terminal devices. Some are *current*-controlled, such as the bipolar transistor, while others are *voltage*-controlled, such as the field effect transistor and the vacuum tube triode. We shall concentrate on the voltage-controlled device because its behavior is simpler to explain.

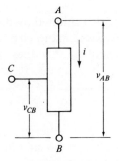

Figure 1-10

Three-Terminal Device

A voltage-controlled three-terminal device is shown in Figure 1-10. Note that there are *three* wires protruding from the device, A, B, and C. The *control* voltage is connected between terminals C and B. We can consider terminals A and B to represent the terminals of a diode. The characteristic curve exhibited by this diode depends upon the value of the control voltage, v_{CB}. As the value of v_{CB} changes, the characteristic of the diode changes. In other words, terminals A and B can behave like a variety of *different* diodes.

The characteristics (note the plural) of a three-terminal device are shown in Figure 1-11. Instead of exhibiting *one* characteristic, as in the

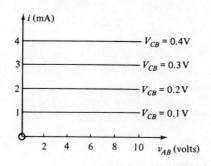

Figure 1-11

Characteristic Curves for a Three-Terminal Device

case of the two-terminal device, the three-terminal device has *many* characteristics. Note that each curve has a label indicating the value of v_{CB} which must be applied in order to obtain that particular characteristic curve. The device whose characteristics are shown in Figure 1-11 is an example of a voltage-controlled device, because it is the control *voltage* that determines the characteristic exhibited by the device. In some devices, it is the *current* that controls. How many characteristics are there in all? Since there are an infinite number of values for v_{CB}, and there is one characteristic for each value of v_{CB}, there are an infinite number of characteristic curves.

EXAMPLE 1-3

In the circuit of Figure 1-10, $V_{AB} = 4$ V and $V_{CB} = 0.1$ V. Determine the value of the current, i, and the resistance of the device between terminals A and B. Use the characteristics of Figure 1-11.

Solution

Since $V_{CB} = 0.1$ V, we use the curve labeled "0.1V." An inspection of

Figure 1-11 reveals that when $V_{AB} = 4$ V, $I = 1$ mA. The resistance, R_{AB}, of the device between terminals A and B is

$$R_{AB} = \frac{V_{AB}}{I} = \frac{4 \text{ V}}{1 \text{ mA}} = 4 \text{ k}\Omega.$$

EXAMPLE 1-4

Repeat Example 1-3 for $V_{CB} = 0.2$ V.

Solution

Since $V_{CB} = 0.2$ V, we use the curve labeled "0.2 V." An inspection of Figure 1-11 reveals that when $V_{AB} = 4$ V, $I = 2$ mA. The resistance, R_{AB}, of the device between terminals A and B is

$$R_{AB} = \frac{V_{AB}}{I} = \frac{4 \text{ V}}{2 \text{ mA}} = 2 \text{ k}\Omega.$$

Note that the control voltage, v_{CB}, controls the *resistance*, R_{AB}, between terminals A and B. By changing v_{CB} from 0.1 V to 0.2 V, we have changed R_{AB} from 4 kΩ to 2 kΩ. We shall return to this important point shortly.

Suppose now that a load resistor is inserted in series with terminals A and B, as shown in Figure 1-12. Remember that it is necessary to draw a load line in order to analyze a nonlinear circuit containing a load resistor.

EXAMPLE 1-5

Determine the values of i and R_{AB} for the circuit of Figure 1-12 if $V_{CB} = 0.1$ V and the characteristic curves of the device are as shown in Figure 1-13.

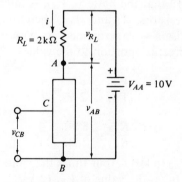

Figure 1-12

Three-Terminal Device in Series with Resistor

Solution

The load line is shown in Figure 1-13. Since $V_{CB} = 0.1$ V, the operating point is located at the intersection of the load line and the characteristic curve labeled "0.1 V," as shown. An inspection of Figure 1-13 reveals that

$$V_{AB} = 8 \text{ V} \qquad V_{R_L} = 2 \text{ V} \qquad I = 1 \text{ mA},$$

$$R_{AB} = \frac{V_{AB}}{I} = \frac{8 \text{ V}}{1 \text{ mA}} = 8 \text{ k}\Omega.$$

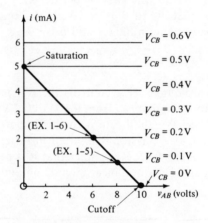

Figure 1-13

Load Line Analysis for Examples 1-5, 1-6, 1-7, and 1-8

Notice in Figure 1-12 that the battery, V_{AA}, is impressed across the series connection of two resistors, R_L and R_{AB}. Therefore, we can say that these two resistors comprise a voltage divider. As with any voltage divider, the voltages divide in direct proportion to the values of the resistors. Thus, we can write

$$\frac{V_{AB}}{V_{R_L}} = \frac{8 \text{ V}}{2 \text{ V}} = \frac{4}{1},$$

and

$$\frac{R_{AB}}{R_L} = \frac{8 \text{ k}\Omega}{2 \text{ k}\Omega} = \frac{4}{1}.$$

Since the value of R_{AB} (8 kΩ) is four times the value of R_L (2 kΩ), the value of V_{AB} (8 V) is four times the value of V_{R_L} (2 V).

EXAMPLE 1-6

Repeat Example 1-5 for $V_{CB} = 0.2$ V.

Solution

Since $V_{CB} = 0.2$ V, the operating point is located at the intersection of the load line and the characteristic curve labeled "0.2 V," as shown in Figure 1-13. An inspection of the figure reveals that

$$V_{AB} = 6 \text{ V} \qquad V_{RL} = 4 \text{ V} \qquad I = 2 \text{ mA},$$

$$R_{AB} = \frac{V_{AB}}{I} = \frac{6 \text{ V}}{2 \text{ mA}} = 3 \text{ k}\Omega.$$

Note that the increase in the value of V_{CB}, from 0.1 V to 0.2 V (for a change of 0.1 V), has resulted in a decrease in the value of R_{AB}, from 8 kΩ to 3 kΩ. This change in R_{AB} has changed the voltage divider ratio so that V_{AB} has decreased from 8 V to 6 V (for a change of 2 V).

$$\frac{V_{AB}}{V_{RL}} = \frac{6 \text{ V}}{4 \text{ V}} = \frac{3}{2},$$

and

$$\frac{R_{AB}}{R_L} = \frac{3 \text{ k}\Omega}{2 \text{ k}\Omega} = \frac{3}{2}.$$

We see, then, that the control voltage varies the value of R_{AB}. As the value of R_{AB} is varied, the voltage divider ratio changes, and consequently, so do the values of V_{AB} and V_{RL}. We shall return to this point in the next section.

EXAMPLE 1-7

Repeat Example 1-5 for $V_{CB} = 0$ V.

Solution

For $V_{CB} = 0$ V, the characteristic curve is flush with the horizontal axis, as shown in Figure 1-13. The operating point is located on the axis, as shown. An inspection of the figure reveals that

$$V_{AB} = 10 \text{ V} = V_{AA} \qquad V_{RL} = 0 \text{ V} \qquad I = 0 \text{ mA},$$

$$R_{AB} = \frac{V_{AB}}{I} = \frac{10 \text{ V}}{0 \text{ mA}} = \infty.$$

We conclude that the device behaves like an open circuit at this point. Since no current flows between terminals A and B, we say that the device is *cutoff*.

EXAMPLE 1-8

Repeat Example 1-5 for $V_{CB} = 0.5$ V.

Solution

Since $V_{CB} = 0.5$ V, the operating point is located at the intersection of the load line and the characteristic curve labeled "0.5 V," as shown in Figure 1-13. An inspection of the figure reveals that

$$V_{AB} = 0 \text{ V} \qquad V_{RL} = 10 \text{ V} = V_{AA} \qquad I = 5 \text{ mA} = \frac{V_{AA}}{R_L},$$

$$R_{AB} = \frac{V_{AB}}{I} = \frac{0 \text{ V}}{5 \text{ mA}} = 0 \ \Omega.$$

Thus, the device behaves like a short circuit at this point. Since the value of R_{AB} is zero, the total battery voltage is impressed across R_L. Note that V_{AB} cannot be smaller than 0 V. Therefore, V_{RL} cannot be larger than V_{AA}. This means that I cannot be larger than V_{AA}/R_L. In other words, there is a certain *maximum* amount of current that can flow through a device in a given circuit. For example, suppose that the value of v_{CB} is increased to 0.6 V. At first thought, you might expect a further increase in current. Notice in Figure 1-13, however, that the load line intersects the curve for $V_{CB} = 0.6$ V at the *same point* that it intersects the curve for $V_{CB} = 0.5$ V. What does this mean? It means that even though v_{CB} is increased above 0.5 V, the current through the device cannot increase above 5 mA. Since the device can hold only a certain amount of current, we say that it becomes *saturated* at 5 mA.

We conclude, then, that v_{CB} can vary the resistance of the device from $R_{AB} = $ infinity, at cutoff, to $R_{AB} = 0$, at saturation. We summarize as follows:

	Cutoff	Saturation
	$V_{AB} = V_{AA}$	$V_{AB} = 0$
	$V_{RL} = 0$	$V_{RL} = V_{AA}$
	$I = 0$	$I = \dfrac{V_{AA}}{R_L}$
	$R_{AB} = \infty$	$R_{AB} = 0$

1-5   The Amplifier

Suppose that v_{CB} is composed of the series connection of a 0.1 V peak sine wave, v_S, and a 0.2 V battery, V_{CC}, as shown in Figure 1-14. The characteristics of the device are shown in Figure 1-15. The control voltage, v_{CB}, is now a complex wave, as shown in Figure 1-16(a). Note that it is a

0.1 V peak sine wave "riding on" a 0.2 V dc level. As can be seen from Figure 1-16(a), the value of v_{CB} varies between 0.1 V and 0.3 V. To see the effects of this variation, let us refer to the characteristics of Figure 1-15. Note that the load line is drawn on the curves. The initial value of

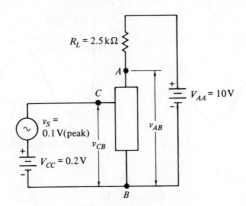

Figure 1-14

An Amplifier

v_{CB} is 0.2 V, its "dc" value, as shown in Figure 1-16(a). Reference to Figure 1-15 reveals that when $v_{CB} = 0.2$ V, the operating point is located at the center of the load line, point X, yielding $V_{AB} = 5$ V. As the value of v_{CB} *increases* from 0.2 V toward 0.3 V, the value of v_{AB} *decreases*. When v_{CB} reaches its maximum value of 0.3 V, v_{AB} reaches its minimum value of

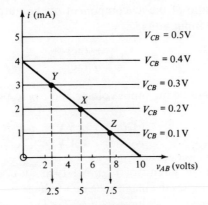

Figure 1-15

Characteristic Curves for a Three-Terminal Device

2.5 V, at point Y in Figure 1-15. As the value of v_{CB} decreases from 0.2 V toward 0.1 V, the value of v_{AB} increases. When v_{CB} reaches its minimum value of 0.1 V, v_{AB} reaches its maximum value of 7.5 V, at point Z in Figure 1-15. The complete waveform of v_{AB} is shown in Figure 1-16(b).

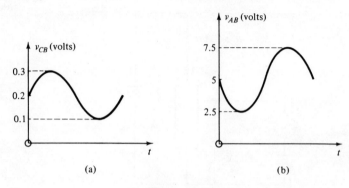

(a)   (b)

Figure 1-16

(a) Waveform of v_{CB}; (b) Waveform of v_{AB}

Now, let us see what has happened. Notice in Figure 1-16 that both v_{CB} and v_{AB} have complex waveforms. This means that each waveform has both a dc component and an ac component. The value of v_{CB} goes 0.1 V below 0.2 V (its dc value) to 0.1 V, and 0.1 V above 0.2 V to 0.3 V. Thus, its ac component is a 0.1 V peak sine wave (v_S). The value of v_{AB} goes 2.5 V below 5 V (its dc value) to 2.5 V, and 2.5 V above 5 V to 7.5 V. Thus, its ac component is a 2.5 V peak sine wave. We define the *voltage gain*, A, of an amplifier as the ratio of the ac component of the output voltage to the ac component of the input voltage.

$$A = \frac{v_O(\text{ac})}{v_I(\text{ac})}. \tag{1-10}$$

If we consider v_{CB} to be the input voltage and v_{AB} to be the output voltage, we can write

$$A = \frac{v_{AB}(\text{ac})}{v_{CB}(\text{ac})} = \frac{2.5 \text{ V}}{0.1 \text{ V}} = 25.$$

Thus, we see that the circuit of Figure 1-14 is an *amplifier*. An amplifier is a circuit that increases the magnitude of a voltage (or current). The circuit of Figure 1-14 provides a voltage gain of 25. This means that the ac component of the *out*put voltage is 25 times larger than the ac component of the *in*put voltage. This is really quit nice. It should be apparent that the amplifier is an extremely useful circuit. It is important to mention that the amplifier *is* the entire circuit of Figure 1-14. The three-terminal device is only one component of the amplifier.

How does the amplifier circuit work? Remember that the control voltage, v_{CB}, controls the resistance, R_{AB}, of the three-terminal device. Thus, we may represent R_{AB} as a variable resistance, as shown in Figure 1-17. R_{AB} is in

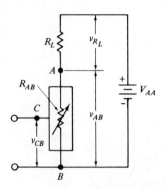

Figure 1-17

Three-Terminal Device Represented as Variable Resistance

series with R_L, and both resistors are connected to the battery, V_{AA}. This battery voltage divides between the two resistors, the divider ratio depending upon the value of R_{AB}. We have seen that only a relatively small change in v_{CB} is necessary to change the value of R_{AB}. As the value of R_{AB} is changed, the voltage divider ratio is varied, resulting in a relatively large redistribution of voltages v_{AB} and v_{R_L}. The changes in the values of v_{AB} and v_{R_L} are relatively large compared with the size of the change in v_{CB}. For example, a 0.1 V change in v_{CB} produced a 2.5 V change in v_{AB} in the amplifier of Figure 1-14. It is the difference in the values of these changes that is responsible for the phenomenon known as voltage gain.

You may be wondering why we have included a 0.2 V battery, V_{CC}, in series with v_S in Figure 1-14. To see the effect of this battery on the performance of the amplifier, let us remove it. If this is done, v_{CB} is no longer a complex wave, but appears as shown in Figure 1-18(a). Note that the dc level is now equal to 0 V. Remember that the characteristic curve for $V_{AB} = 0$ V is flush with the horizontal axis. Therefore, the dc level of v_{AB} is equal to V_{AA} (10 V), as shown at point X in Figure 1-18(b). We say that the device is biased at cutoff. As v_{CB} increases from 0 V toward +0.1 V, v_{AB} decreases from 10 V toward 7.5 V (for a change of 2.5 V) as shown at point Y in Figure 1-18(b). As v_{CB} decreases from 0 V toward −0.1 V, however, v_{AB} *tries* to increase from 10 V toward 12.5 V (for a change of 2.5 V). Notice that we use the term "tries." We have seen that the value of v_{AB} cannot become larger than the battery voltage, V_{AA} (10 V, in this case).

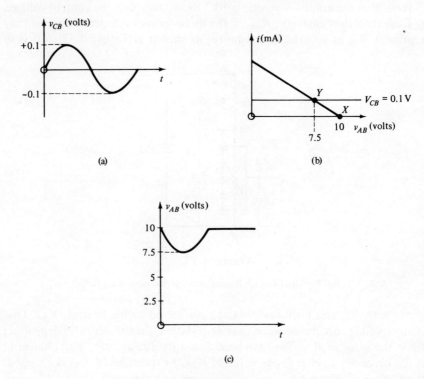

(a)   (b)

(c)

Figure 1-18

(a) Waveform of v_{CB} with $V_{CC} = 0$ V; (b) Load Line Analysis with $V_{CC} = 0$ V; (c) Waveform of v_{AB} with $V_{CC} = 0$ V

Therefore, the value of v_{AB} remains equal to 10 V during this half-cycle. The resulting waveform of v_{AB} is shown in Figure 1-18(c).

Note that although the input waveform (v_{CB}) is a sine wave, the output (v_{AB}) is *not*; that is, the output waveform is only *half* a sine wave. An amplifier must not only stretch the magnitude of a voltage, *it must also retain the same waveshape.* Therefore, the behavior exhibited in Figure 1-18(c) is totally unacceptable. We see, then, that we must avoid biasing the device at cutoff. A little thought will reveal that a similar situation would develop if we were to bias the device at saturation.

It would seem that we should like the dc operating point of v_{AB} to be someplace between saturation ($V_{AB} = 0$ V) and cutoff ($V_{AB} = V_{AA}$). This would allow v_{AB} to "swing" both above and below its dc level. The only way to accomplish this is to have v_{CB} begin at some value above zero. It is for this reason that a V_{CC} battery was placed in series with v_S in Figure 1-14. Obviously, the best place to select the dc operating point is in the center of the load line, as in Figure 1-15. This allows for maximum swing in both the positive and negative directions.

It should also be mentioned that the amplifier will not function without the presence of battery V_{AA}. It is V_{AA} which powers the voltage divider composed of R_{AB} and R_L. Without this battery, we get no voltage divider action, and thus, no amplification. Therefore, we conclude that all amplifiers must be supplied with dc power.

It was mentioned that the gain of an amplifier is the ratio of the ac output voltage to the ac input voltage. The gain of the amplifier of Figure 1-14 is 25. Thus, if $v_I = 0.1$ V, $v_O = 2.5$ V, and if $v_I = 0.2$ V, $v_O = 5$ V, and so on. Note that the output appears to be directly proportional to the input. Suppose we set $v_I = 1$ V. Then it *appears* as though v_O will be equal to 25 V. If the dc value of v_{AB} is 5 V, v_{AB} will *try* to go 25 V above 5 V to 30 V, and 25 V below 5 V to -20 V, as shown by the dashed lines in Figure 1-19. We

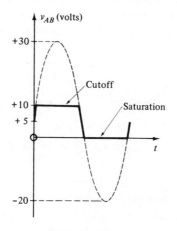

Figure 1-19

Waveform of v_{AB} for Overdriven Amplifier

know, however, that v_{AB} can be no larger than $V_{AA} = 10$ V (cutoff) and no smaller than 0 V (saturation). Thus, the actual waveform of v_{AB} (solid curve in Figure 1-19) is *clipped*. Since the output waveform is not a sine wave, we say that it is *distorted*, or twisted out of shape. When the input to the amplifier is 1 V, the amplifier cannot produce a 25 V sine wave at the output, and thus we say that the amplifier is being *over driven*. The important point here is that the output voltage of an amplifier is directly proportional to the input voltage *only up to a certain point*. This is the point at which the output waveform distorts.

The maximum sinusoidal output that an amplifier can produce is limited by the size of battery V_{AA}. Why not increase the size of the battery? We cannot increase the size of the battery indefinitely because the three-terminal device has a specific voltage rating which, if exceeded, can result in permanent damage to the device. What is the largest voltage that can be applied to the input of the amplifier of Figure 1-14 before the output waveform distorts? The largest peak value that the output of the amplifier can produce is 5 V (from 5 V to 10 V and from 5 V to 0 V). The peak value of the input voltage that will produce this output is

$$v_I = \frac{v_O}{A} = \frac{5 \text{ V}}{25} = 0.2 \text{ V}.$$

We conclude that the largest voltage that can be amplified by the amplifier of Figure 1-14 is 0.2 V.

If we apply a 1 mV peak sine wave to the input terminals of the amplifier of Figure 1-14, the output voltage will be 25 mV. If we want a larger output, we can take the output voltage from the first amplifier and apply it to the input terminals of a second amplifier, as shown in Figure 1-20. Thus, the

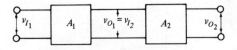

Figure 1-20

Cascaded Amplifier Stages

output voltage of A_1 (v_{O_1}) now becomes the input voltage to A_2 (v_{I_2}). If the second amplifier has the same gain as the first, the output voltage of the second amplifier (v_{O_2}) is

$$v_{O_2} = A_2 v_{I_2} = A_2 v_{O_1} = (25)(25 \text{ mV}) = 625 \text{ mV}.$$

Thus, we can increase the size of the signal by connecting the amplifiers as shown in Figure 1-20. Amplifiers connected in this manner are said to be connected in *cascade*. Each individual amplifier is called a *stage* of amplification. The two-stage amplifier of Figure 1-20 is called a *multistage* amplifier.

If A_1 is the gain of the first stage and A_2 is the gain of the second, we can write

$$v_{O_2} = A_2 v_{I_2} = A_2 v_{O_1} = A_2 A_1 v_{I_1}. \tag{1-11}$$

The *overall* gain of a multistage amplifier is the ratio of the output voltage of the last stage to the input voltage of the first.

$$\text{Overall gain} = \frac{v_{O_2}}{v_{I_1}} = \frac{A_2 A_1 v_{I_1}}{v_{I_1}} = A_1 A_2. \tag{1-12}$$

Equation (1-12) says that the overall gain of a multistage amplifier is equal to the product of the gains of the individual stages. We see, then, that we can obtain very large values of gain by cascading a large number of stages.

1-6   The Modern Op Amp

Now that you have some understanding of the behavior of an amplifier, you are ready for a discussion of the modern op amp. The term "op amp" is an abbreviation for *operational* amplifier. The operational amplifier is a special type of circuit that has many applications, particularly in analog computers. The term "operational" is used because this type of amplifier has a circuit configuration that enables it to perform many arithmetic and mathematical operations, such as addition, integration, and so on.

The operational amplifier, like most other types of amplifiers, is composed of *discrete* circuit components. By this we mean that the circuit is made up of separate and distinct entities, such as transistors, resistors, capacitors, and so on all connected together by lengths of wire. Generally speaking, the design of an amplifier such as this involves a number of specific steps.

1.   The general circuit configuration is determined. This configuration

Figure 1-21

Circuit Board (Courtesy of Wavetek)

depends upon the specifications of the system into which the amplifier is to be inserted.
2.   A tentative design is worked out on paper.
3.   The components are purchased.
4.   The circuit is "breadboarded." A breadboard is a nonpermanent structure which is built to test the performance of the circuit.

Figure 1-22

Modern Op Amp (Courtesy of Melcor)

5.   The circuit undergoes environmental testing.
6.   The final wiring is laid out on a circuit board.
7.   The final product is inserted into the system and its performance is checked.

This process may take weeks or months. The completed circuit is constructed on a circuit board, as shown in Figure 1-21. Note that the circuit is composed of a number of discrete components.

The operational amplifier has been around for a long time. In recent years, however, the term "op amp" has come to acquire a different meaning. Due to recent advances in technology, it has become feasible to manufacture an entire multistage amplifier in a very small package, as shown in Figure 1-22. This package has acquired the name "op amp." Strictly speaking, there are three types of op amps presently being manufactured. They are the discrete, the integrated circuit (IC), and the hybrid. Figure 1-23 shows a number of different types. The larger, box-type units in the background are the discretes, whereas the smaller packages in the foreground are the IC's and hybrids.

The *discrete* op amp, as the name implies, is composed entirely of separate components, much the same as the circuit board discussed previously. What

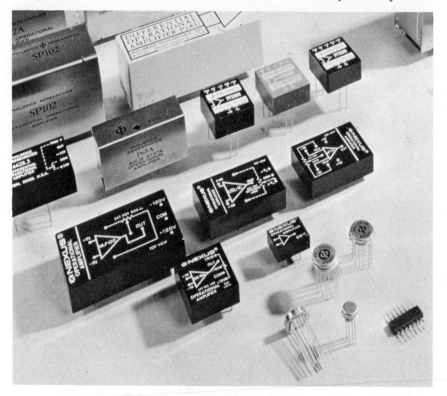

Figure 1-23

Types of Op Amps (Courtesy of Philbrick)

sets this device apart is that it is specially designed and packaged, and sold as a complete unit. It generally comes in a box-type package, as shown in Figure 1-24(a). Notice in Figure 1-24(b) that the inside of the box contains discrete components. Since it is specially designed, the discrete op amp has

(a)   (b)

Figure 1-24

(a) Discrete Op Amp Package; (b) Interior of Package (Courtesy of Union Carbide)

extremely high performance (we shall discuss what is meant by high performance later), but is also expensive compared to the other types of op amps.

At the other end of the spectrum is the *integrated circuit* (*IC*) op amp, or *monolithic chip*. The word "monolithic" means that the entire amplifier, including transistors, resistors, and so on, is fabricated on a *single* silicon chip. It is called an integrated circuit because the entire circuit is integrated, or combined in one piece. The size of the *IC*, which contains a multistage amplifier, is approximately the same size as a single discrete transistor! Since a multistage amplifier is the equivalent of *many* transistors and resistors, you can now appreciate the extent of the advance of technology. The advantages of the *IC* op amp are its extremely small size, low price, and adaptability to mass production techniques. However, it does not as yet have the high performance of the discrete op amp, and is thus used in less critical applications. Figure 1-25 shows three types of packages in which the *IC* op amp is manufactured.

Finally, as the name implies, the *hybrid* op amp is a combination of both the discrete and the *IC*. In other words, it contains both discrete components and chips.

The advantages of the modern op amp are summarized as follows:

1. Due to the small package, the use of the modern op amp permits significant savings in *size* and *weight*. This makes it ideal for applications where space is at a premium, such as in airplanes, missiles, and space capsules.

(b)

(a)

(c)

Figure 1-25

Types of *IC* Packages: (a) *TO* Package; (b) Flat Package; (c) Dual In-Line Package
(Courtesy of Motorola)

2. Since the unit is manufactured and purchased as a single package, the user saves a considerable amount of *time* which would otherwise be spent in design, layout, testing and so on. This time can be used for a

more detailed analysis of the system into which the amplifier is to be inserted. In addition, it is generally *cheaper* to buy a specially designed amplifier than to design it yourself.

3. The special design of the unit allows the selection of matched components for good *temperature stability*. This stability is particularly good in the case of the *IC* op amp, where the components are part of the same chip and are thus at the same temperature. We shall hear more about this later.

4. The design of the modern op amp contributes to a considerable degree of *flexibility*. We shall see that the unit can be used as a dc amplifier, ac amplifier, differential amplifier, inverting amplifier, or noninverting amplifier.

5. The op amp can be used in *applications* other than amplifiers, as shown in Chapter 9.

6. The op amp has a high degree of *reliability* due to the small number of components. This means that there is a relatively small probability of failure.

7. Since there are fewer interconnecting wires, there is less stray capacitance. This means that there are fewer *time delays* encountered in passing a signal through a system containing op amps.

8. Finally, we shall see that the single package nature of the op amp dictates an entirely new philosophy of circuit analysis. This new analytical philosophy makes it easier for *nonelectronically trained* personnel to work with op amps.

For these reasons, the op amp is becoming more and more popular with engineers.

SUMMARY

1.   A characteristic curve is a graph of the current through a device versus the voltage across it.

2.   A diode is a two-terminal device whose resistance depends upon the polarity of the voltage impressed across its terminals.

3.   It is necessary to use the graphical load line technique to analyze nonlinear circuits.

4.   A three-terminal device is one whose characteristic curve is controlled by a voltage or current.

5.   An amplifier is a circuit that magnifies the size of a voltage or current.

6.   Because it is manufactured in a single package, the modern op amp has many advantages.

PROBLEMS

1-1.   Compute the value of the resistance for each of the four devices whose characteristic curves are shown in Figure 1-26.

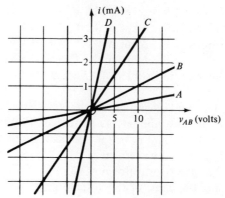

Figure 1-26

Characteristic Curves for Problem 1-1

1-2.   Compute the resistance of the diode whose characteristic curve is shown in Figure 1-6 when:

   (a) $v_{AB} = 0.3$ V

   (b) $v_{AB} = 0.5$ V

   (c) $v_{AB} = 0.7$ V

   (d) $v_{AB} = 1$ V

   (e) $v_{AB} = 1.2$ V.

1-3.   The diode whose characteristic curve is shown in Figure 1-9 is connected in series with a 10 V battery and a 2.5 kΩ resistor. Determine the values of:

   (a) V_{AB}

   (b) V_{R_L}

   (c) I

   (d) R_{AB}.

1-4.   Repeat Problem 1-3, except make $V_{AA} = 8$ V.

1-5.   Repeat Problem 1-3, except make $V_{AA} = 6$ V.

1-6.   Repeat Problem 1-3, except make $V_{AA} = 10$ V and $R_L = 3$ kΩ.

1-7.   Repeat Problem 1-6, except make $R_L = 4$ kΩ.

1-8.   Repeat Problem 1-6, except make $R_L = 5$ kΩ.

1-9.   Terminals A and B of the three-terminal device whose characteristics are shown in Figure 1-11 are connected in series with an 8 V battery and a 2 kΩ resistor. If $V_{CB} = 0.1$ V, compute the values of:

   (a) V_{AB}

   (b) V_{RL}

   (c) I

   (d) R_{AB}.

1-10.   Repeat Problem 1-9, except make $V_{CB} = 0.2$ V.

1-11.   Repeat Problem 1-9, except make $V_{CB} = 0.3$ V.

1-12.   Repeat Problem 1-9, except make $V_{CB} = 0.4$ V.

1-13.   Repeat Problem 1-9, except make $V_{CB} = 0.5$ V.

Explain why the answers to Problem 1-13 are the same as those of Problem 1-12.

1-14.   The three-terminal device whose characteristics are shown in Figure 1-11 is connected as an amplifier, as shown in Figure 1-14. $V_{AA} = 8$ V, $R_L = 2$ kΩ, $V_{CC} = 0.2$ V, and v_S is a 0.1 V peak sine wave.

   (a) Sketch a labeled waveform of v_{CB}.

   (b) Sketch a labeled waveform of v_{AB}.

   (c) Compute the value of the voltage gain.

1-15.   Repeat Problem 1-14, except make v_S a 0.2 V peak sine wave.

1-16.   Repeat Problem 1-15, except make $V_{CC} = 0.3$ V.

Explain why the waveform of v_{AB} is distorted.

1-17.   Repeat Problem 1-14, except make $V_{CC} = 0$ V.

Explain why the waveform of v_{AB} is distorted.

1-18.   Repeat Problem 1-14, except make $V_{CC} = 0.4$ V.

Explain why the waveform of v_{AB} is distorted.

1-19.   Repeat Problem 1-14, except make v_S a 0.3 V peak sine wave. Explain why the waveform of v_{AB} is distorted.

1-20.   Three amplifier stages are connected in cascade. Their gains are 18, 30, and 20. Compute the value of the overall gain.

1-21.   For the multistage amplifier of Problem 1-20, compute the peak value of the input sine wave which will result in a 2 V peak sine wave at the output.

2

The Black Box

Suppose that you have decided to build a small wooden cabinet. You would lay out plans for the structure and buy the necessary materials. In addition, you would have to develop skill with certain tools, such as the hammer, screwdriver, plane, and so on. It would be impossible to begin work on the cabinet without first knowing how to use these tools. Similarly, before we discuss the op amp it is necessary to develop a new analytical tool. This tool becomes extremely important when we set out to study the practical op amp in Chapter 3. In previous studies, you have learned to analyze complex circuits by making use of Ohm's law, Kirchhoff's laws, Thevenin's theorem, and Norton's theorem. Although we shall continue to utilize these techniques, our object here is to consider a *new* technique, or tool, one which is of particular use in the analysis and design of op amp circuits. This chapter deals with the study of this new technique.

2-1 The Black Box

In the last chapter we saw that it is possible to construct a multistage amplifier. Each individual stage in this amplifier contains a three-terminal

31

device. The three-terminal device is usually either a bipolar transistor, as shown in Figure 2-1(a), or a field effect transistor, as shown in Figure 2-1(b). Amplifiers composed of discrete components are generally analyzed using a circuit model known as the small-signal equivalent circuit. The first step

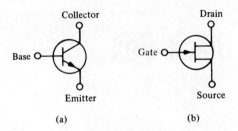

(a)   (b)

Figure 2-1

Symbol for: (a) Bipolar Transistor; (b) Field Effect Transistor

in the analysis of a multistage amplifier is the drawing of the small-signal equivalent circuit. Next, the various voltages and currents are computed utilizing Ohm's and Kirchhoff's laws, and Thevenin's and Norton's theorems. Finally, the output voltage or current is compared with the input, and the gain is computed. This technique is an extremely powerful tool; it facilitates considerably the analysis of discrete component amplifier circuits. The modern op amp, because it is manufactured and sold as a *single* package, lends itself to a simpler, more direct method of analysis.

Whether it is a discrete, hybrid, or *IC*, the op amp must be treated as a *single unit*. From this point on in the text we shall represent the op amp as a *black box*, as shown in Figure 2-2. In other words, we shall consider the

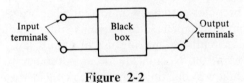

Figure 2-2

The Black Box

circuitry which comprises the op amp to be enclosed within the box. The word "black" is used to indicate that we are not so much interested in what is *in*side the box as we are in its behavior at its input and output terminals. We shall elaborate on this last point shortly. Since the op amp is an amplifier, it has both a pair of input and output terminals, as shown in Figure 2-2.

It should be mentioned that the black box technique of analysis can be applied to circuits other than op amps. It can be applied to simple passive circuits containing resistors, capacitors, inductors, and so on; it can be applied to transistors (the transistor can be represented by a black box composed of four *h*-parameters); it can be applied to *non*electrical systems, where the input and output terminals receive nonelectrical signals (such as a shaft rotation, or a pressure change, or a beam of light). Thus, many of the principles and techniques developed in this text have significance beyond the electronics field. However, the black box technique of analysis is particularly useful when dealing with op amps.

2-2   The Z-Parameters

We are now ready for a more detailed study of the black box. Before proceeding, it should be mentioned that the black box is sometimes referred to as a 4-terminal network, a 4-pole (pole is an alternate word for terminal), or a 2-port, as shown in Figure 2-3. A port represents a *pair* of terminals; thus a 4-terminal network has two pairs of terminals and is called a 2-*port*.

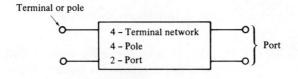

Figure 2-3

A Four-Terminal Network

At this point, we ask the reader to accept a proposition. The proposition is as follows: It is not necessary that we know *exactly* what is inside the black box in order to analyze its behavior. It is true, as mentioned in the previous section, that if we knew the exact circuit within the black box, we could perform an analysis utilizing the various circuit laws and theorems. However, much time can be saved if we represent the *interior* of the black box by a series of quantities known as "parameters."

Every 4-terminal network can be uniquely represented by a set of four parameters. A parameter is a term whose numerical value depends upon the circuitry within the black box. There are many types of parameters that can be used to represent the interior of the black box. There are Z-parameters, Y-parameters, *h*-parameters, and others. Because of the nature of their interiors, some black boxes are more conveniently represented by one set of parameters than by another. For example, the transistor, because of its current-amplifying ability, is generally represented by a set of four *h*-parameters. Each black box has its "own" set of four parameters. These parameters are *constants* for any given black box; they depend entirely upon what is *in*side the box. Once the values of the four parameters for any given black box are known, all of the voltages and currents at the terminals of the box can be computed. The parameters can have units of resistance or conductance, or they can be dimensionless.

Refer now to Figure 2-4. A voltage, V_1, is applied directly to the input terminals of the black box. This voltage causes a current, I_1, to flow *into*

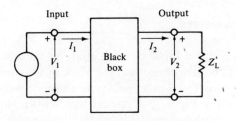

Figure 2-4

Input and Output Quantities of the Black Box

the input terminals of the box. V_1 and I_1 in turn cause a current, I_2, to flow *out* of the output terminals of the box and a voltage, V_2, is developed across the output terminals. V_2 is developed across the load impedance, Z_L, which is connected across the output terminals. At this point, we shall not distinguish between dc and ac quantities, and thus, the voltages and currents are represented by capital letters.

Whether it be discrete, hybrid, or *IC*, the op amp is most conveniently represented by a set of four *Z*-parameters. They are

$$Z_{11}$$
$$Z_{12}$$
$$Z_{21}$$
$$Z_{22}.$$

The values of the currents and voltages (V_1, I_1, I_2, and V_2) indicated in Figure 2-4 depend upon the values of these four *Z*-parameters. The values of the *Z*-parameters depend in turn upon the circuitry within the black box. Note that we are concerned only with "terminal" quantities; that is, the currents and voltages indicated are those at the input and output terminals of the box.

To study further the relationship between the parameters and the terminal quantities, it can be shown that we can write the following two equations:

$$V_1 = Z_{11}I_1 + Z_{12}I_2, \tag{2-1}$$

$$V_2 = Z_{21}I_1 - Z_{22}I_2. \tag{2-2}$$

In these equations, V_1, I_1, I_2, and V_2 represent the terminal quantities and Z_{11}, Z_{12}, Z_{21}, and Z_{22} represent the four Z-parameters. Let us now examine these equations more closely. Equation (2-1) states that V_1 is equal to the *sum* (note plus sign) of two voltages; these voltages are $Z_{11}I_1$ and $Z_{12}I_2$. Examining the first voltage, we see that this voltage can be considered as a voltage drop across an impedance, Z_{11}, due to a current, I_1. Since I_1 is the current that flows into the input terminals of the black box, we can place an impedance equal to Z_{11} in series with these input terminals, as shown in Figure 2-5. The second voltage, $Z_{12}I_2$, is the voltage drop across an impedance, Z_{12}, due to a current, I_2. However, this second voltage, although it is due to I_2, must appear in series with the *in*put terminals since V_1 (the voltage across the input terminals) must be equal to the sum of the two voltages [see Equation (2-1)]. Therefore, the second voltage, $Z_{12}I_2$, is represented as a "controlled" voltage generator in series with the input terminals as shown in Figure 2-5. We say that the value of this generator is controlled by the value of I_2.

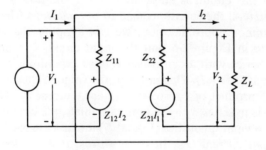

Figure 2-5

The Z-Parameters

Similarly, Equation (2-2) states that V_2 is equal to the *difference* (note minus sign) of two voltages; these voltages are $Z_{21}I_1$ and $Z_{22}I_2$. The first voltage, $Z_{21}I_1$, is a voltage drop across Z_{21} due to current I_1. This voltage must appear in series with the *out*put terminals and is thus represented by a controlled voltage generator, $Z_{21}I_1$, as shown in Figure 2-5. The value of this generator is controlled by the value of I_1. The second voltage, $Z_{22}I_2$, is the voltage drop across impedance Z_{22} due to current I_2. Thus, we place an impedance equal to Z_{22} in series with the output terminals as shown in Figure 2-5.

Figure 2-5 shows the completed circuit. All of the Z's have units of impedance; that is, they are all measured in ohms. Note that the Z-parameters relate the various *terminal* quantities (V_1, I_1, I_2, and V_2) to one another. We shall see shortly that these terminal quantities are the only ones which concern us when we are dealing with the black box method of analysis. The four Z-parameters represent the circuitry within the interior of the box. Their values depend entirely upon this circuitry.

Refer again to Figure 2-5. Note that the input circuit is represented by an impedance in series with a controlled voltage generator. Does this mean that if we were to look inside the box we would see an actual impedance connected in series with a generator? Maybe, and maybe not. It depends upon the nature of the particular black box we are dealing with. By this point, the reader should realize that we simply do not care about what specifically is inside the box. As long as we know the values of the four Z-parameters, we have enough information to analyze the circuit. In the next chapter, we shall see that the circuitry within the op amp is composed of a multistage transistor amplifier. This is considerably more complex than the simple equivalent of Figure 2-5.

We turn our attention now to an actual analysis of the circuit of Figure 2-5. Although this circuit is an accurate representation of the black box using Z-parameters, the equations tend to become somewhat involved. By making one minor approximation, we can simplify the equations considerably. Note in Figure 2-5 that the input circuit is represented by an impedance in series with a controlled voltage generator. The value of the generator is equal to $Z_{12}I_2$. This says that the value of the generator voltage is equal to the product of parameter Z_{12} and current I_2. Therefore, since this generator is in series with the input terminals, the circuit of Figure 2-5 implies that the *in*put quantities (V_1 and I_1) are at least partially dependent upon the *out*put current (I_2). In other words, there is some "feedback" mechanism within the black box that makes the input circuit somewhat dependent upon what is happening at the output. This is generally true of all black boxes. Because of the internal circuitry of the practical op amp, however, the dependence of the input quantities upon those at the output is relatively slight. Therefore, we shall assume that *parameter Z_{12} is approximately equal to zero*. But if Z_{12} is equal to zero, then controlled generator $Z_{12}I_2$ is also equal to zero. Thus, a simplified version of the circuit can be redrawn in Figure 2-6. Note that the input circuit is now composed only of Z_{11}.

Since V_1 is applied directly across the input terminals, and Z_{11} is the only impedance in series with these terminals, V_1 is the voltage across Z_{11}. Thus, the input current, I_1, can be computed by Ohm's law:

$$I_1 = \frac{V_1}{Z_{11}}. \tag{2-3}$$

Note that the output circuit in Figure 2-6 has a controlled voltage generator whose value is equal to $Z_{21}I_1$. This means that there is a voltage generated

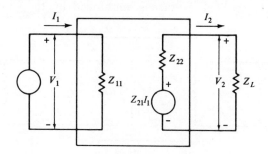

Figure 2-6

Approximate Equivalent Circuit

in the *out*put circuit which is directly proportional to the *in*put current, I_1. We can rewrite the value of this controlled voltage generator as follows:

$$Z_{21}I_1 = Z_{21}\left(\frac{V_1}{Z_{11}}\right) = \left(\frac{Z_{21}}{Z_{11}}\right)V_1. \tag{2-4}$$

This shows that the value of this controlled voltage generator can be considered as being directly proportional to the input *voltage*, V_1 as well as to the current.

We shall now redefine some quantities. Since impedance Z_{11} can be considered as being connected across the input terminals of the black box (see Figure 2-6), we can say that Z_{11} is equal to the *input impedance*, Z_I, of the box. Similarly, V_1 is the *input voltage*, V_I, and I_1 is the *input current*, I_I. These relationships are summarized as follows:

$$Z_{11} = Z_I = \text{input impedance of the black box}$$

$$V_1 = V_I = \text{input voltage to the black box}$$

$$I_1 = I_I = \text{input current to the black box.}$$

In addition, we shall redefine the factor (Z_{21}/Z_{11}) as the *voltage gain*, A, Z_{22} as the *output impedance*, Z_0, V_2 as the *output voltage*, V_0, and I_2 as the *output current*, I_0. These relationships are now summarized:

$$(Z_{21}/Z_{11}) = A = \text{the voltage gain of the black box}$$
$$Z_{22} = Z_O = \text{the output impedance of the black box}$$
$$V_2 = V_O = \text{the output voltage of the black box}$$
$$I_2 = I_O = \text{the output current of the black box.}$$

The circuit with which we shall be working from this point on is shown in Figure 2-7. Notice that an input voltage, V_I, is applied to the input terminals of the box. This voltage is multiplied by the gain, A, in the

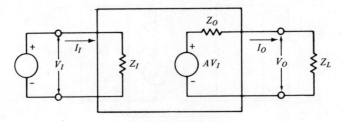

Figure 2-7

Alternate Form of Equivalent Circuit

output circuit. Thus, there is a controlled voltage generator, AV_I, in the output circuit; the value of this generator is directly proportional to both A and V_I. The controlled generator is connected in series with the output impedance, Z_O. Thus, we can consider the series combination of AV_I and Z_O as comprising a voltage *source*, where AV_I is the generated voltage and Z_O is the internal impedance of the source. The actual output voltage, V_O, will be somewhat less than AV_I because of the voltage divider action between Z_O and Z_L.

2-3　Applications of the Black Box

We have now reduced the representation of the interior of the black box to the following three parameters:

$$Z_I$$
$$A$$
$$Z_O.$$

We shall next illustrate the proper technique to be used in analyzing black box circuits. Refer to Figure 2-8. Note that a source voltage, V_S, is connected through a source impedance, Z_S, to the input terminals of the box. This source impedance might represent the internal impedance of the source (where the source is composed of both V_S and Z_S, as in a transducer), or it may be some impedance *intentionally* inserted in series with V_S in order to

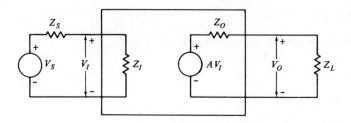

Figure 2-8

Practical Equivalent Circuit

achieve some desired effect (this will be discussed in a following chapter). A load impedance, Z_L, is connected across the output terminals. Now, here is an important point: Notice in Figure 2-8 that Z_I, AV_I, and Z_O are all located *in*side the box to symbolize the fact that they are part of the box. On the other hand, V_S, Z_S, and Z_L are *out*side the box, indicating that they represent components that are not part of the op amp. Now let us illustrate a problem-solving technique for the circuit of Figure 2-8.

EXAMPLE 2-1

The following values are given for the parameters and components of Figure 2-8:

$$Z_I = 10 \text{ k}\Omega \qquad V_S = 1 \text{ mV}$$
$$A = 1000 \qquad Z_S = 0$$
$$Z_O = 50 \text{ }\Omega \qquad Z_L = 1 \text{ k}\Omega$$

Compute the value of the output voltage, V_O.

Solution

Note first that $Z_S = 0$. This means that the source generator, V_S, is applied directly to the input terminals of the box, so that $V_I = V_S$.

$$V_I = V_S = 1 \text{ mV}.$$

Next, we must compute the value of the controlled voltage generator, AV_I.

$$AV_I = 1000(1 \text{ mV}) = 1000 \text{ mV} = 1 \text{ V}.$$

Finally, we see that V_O will be somewhat less than AV_I because of the voltage divider action between Z_O and Z_L. Using the voltage divider formula, we get

$$V_O = \frac{(AV_I)Z_L}{Z_O + Z_L} = \frac{(1 \text{ V})(1000)}{50 + 1000} = 0.95 \text{ V}.$$

EXAMPLE 2-2

Repeat Example 2-1, except make $Z_O = 100 \ \Omega$.

Solution

We proceed as in Example 2-1:

$$V_S = V_I = 1 \text{ mV},$$

$$AV_I = 1000(1 \text{ mV}) = 1000 \text{ mV} = 1 \text{ V},$$

$$V_O = \frac{(AV_I)Z_L}{Z_O + Z_L} = \frac{(1 \text{ V})(1000)}{100 + 1000} = 0.91 \text{ V}.$$

Notice that the value of V_O in Example 2-2 (0.91 V) is *less* than in Example 2-1 (0.95 V). This occurs because the value of Z_O is *larger* in Example 2-2 (100 Ω) than Example 2-1 (50 Ω). A larger value of Z_O means that more voltage will be dropped across this resistance, with a correspondingly smaller amount dropped across the output terminals. Therefore, in order to obtain a *large* value of output voltage, V_O, we should like the value of Z_O to be as *small* as possible.

EXAMPLE 2-3

Repeat Example 2-2, except make $Z_S = 1 \ \text{k}\Omega$.

Solution

Now that Z_S is no longer equal to zero, V_I is no longer equal to V_S. V_I will now be somewhat smaller than V_S because of the voltage divider action between Z_S and Z_I (see Figure 2-8). To compute the value of V_I, we must apply the voltage divider formula to the input circuit of Figure 2-8:

$$V_I = \frac{(V_S)Z_I}{Z_S + Z_I} = \frac{(1 \text{ mV})(10,000)}{1000 + 10,000} = 0.91 \text{ mV}.$$

Proceeding as in Example 2-2, we get

$$AV_I = 1000 \ (0.91 \text{ mV}) = 910 \text{ mV} = 0.91 \text{ V},$$

$$V_O = \frac{(AV_I)Z_L}{Z_O + Z_L} = \frac{(0.91 \text{ V})(1000)}{100 + 1000} = 0.83 \text{ V}.$$

Notice that the value of V_O in Example 2-3 (0.83 V) is *less* than in Example 2-2 (0.91 V). The value of V_O is smaller because the value of AV_I is smaller (0.91 V instead of 1 V). The value of AV_I is smaller because the value of V_I is smaller (0.91 mV instead of 1 mV). The reason that V_I is smaller in Example 2-3 than in Example 2-2 is that, because of the voltage divider consisting of Z_S and Z_I, some of the voltage from source generator V_S is "lost" across Z_S. Reference to Figure 2-8 reveals that only the voltage appearing across the input terminals of the box (V_I) is multiplied by A; that is, the value of the controlled voltage generator is equal to AV_I, *not* AV_S. Since the input circuit is composed of a voltage divider, we can obtain a large value of V_I by making Z_I large. Therefore, in order to obtain a *large* value of V_I (and hence, V_O), we should like the value of Z_I to be as *large* as possible.

In most practical design problems, we are given a source (comprised of V_S and Z_S) and a load (Z_L). We are required to design an op amp that will amplify the source voltage and deliver this amplified voltage to the load. This means that the values of V_S, Z_S, and Z_L are *fixed* before the selection and design of the op amp is begun; that is, these values cannot be changed by the designer. Therefore, *only* the op amp and its associated circuitry may be manipulated to optimize the design. It should now be apparent from the results of the previous discussion that for given values of V_S, Z_S, and Z_L, we can maximize the values of V_O as follows:

1.   Make the value of Z_I as large as possible.
2.   Make the value of A as large as possible.
3.   Make the value of Z_O as small as possible.

How is this done? As previously mentioned, the values of these three parameters are dependent upon the circuitry within the op amp. The optimization of these parameters is a task for the op amp manufacturers and will not concern us here.

SUMMARY

1.   The entire op amp is located within the black box and must be treated as a single unit.
2.   We can represent the interior of the box by four Z-parameters. The values of these parameters are dependent upon the circuitry within the box.
3.   We are interested only in the behavior at the terminals of the box and not specifically in what is inside it.
4. As a result of our approximations, we need know only three quantities (Z_I, A, and Z_O) to describe completely the interior of the box.

PROBLEMS

2-1. The following values are given for the circuit of Figure 2-8:

$$Z_I = 20 \text{ k}\Omega \qquad V_S = 0.5 \text{ mV}$$
$$A = 5000 \qquad Z_S = 500 \text{ }\Omega$$
$$Z_O = 200 \text{ }\Omega \qquad Z_L = 5 \text{ k}\Omega$$

Compute the value of the output voltage, V_O.

2-2. (a) Repeat Problem 2-1, except make $Z_O = 800 \text{ }\Omega$.
(b) Explain why the value of V_O changed.

2-3. (a) Repeat Problem 2-1, except make $Z_I = 8 \text{ k}\Omega$.
(b) Explain why the value of V_O changed.

2-4. (a) Repeat Problem 2-1, except make $A = 8000$.
(b) Explain why the value of V_O changed.

2-5. The source and load values for a particular design are given below:

$$V_S = 3.5 \text{ mV} \qquad Z_S = 250 \text{ }\Omega \qquad Z_L = 600 \text{ }\Omega$$

A manufacturer produces a series of different op amps, all with the same Z_I (15 kΩ) and Z_O (150 Ω), but with different values of A. What value of A is required if it is desired that $V_O = 10$ V?

2-6. Repeat Problem 2-5 if it is desired that $V_O = 2$ V.

2-7. Suppose that the value of Z_L is increased from 600 Ω to 800 Ω in Problem 2-5. Should the value of A be increased or decreased if it is desired that V_O remain equal to 10 V? Explain.

2-8. Repeat Problem 2-7 if the value of Z_S is increased from 250 Ω to 1 kΩ.

3

The Practical
Op Amp

At this point, the reader may be losing patience. Why study the black box? Why is it necessary to understand the black box concept in order to be able to analyze op amps? The answer is that the black box concept is an indispensable *tool* whose use must be learned before one can deal effectively with op amps. Just as a carpenter must learn how to use a hammer before he can build a cabinet, so must the engineer or technician understand the use of the black box concept before he can analyze practical op amp circuits. Having handled this new tool in some detail in Chapter 2, we are now ready for a study of the practical op amp. In this chapter, we shall deal with some of the aspects of the practical op amp. We shall utilize the black box technique as an aid in demonstrating the proper analytical methods to be used with these devices.

3-1 The Op Amp Package

Whether it is a discrete, hybrid, or *IC*, the modern op amp is manufactured and sold in a single package. As shown in Chapter 1, the size and shape of the package depend upon the type of op amp (discrete, hybrid, or

IC), as well as the use for which it is intended. In any case, the modern op amp package is a small unit with approximately eight to ten leads portruding from its case. Each of these leads runs to a particular portion of the op amp circuit *in*side the package. We shall now discuss the function of each of these leads.

Figure 3-1 shows a schematic diagram of the Fairchild μA702A high gain, wideband dc amplifier. This unit is a dc amplifier which is constructed

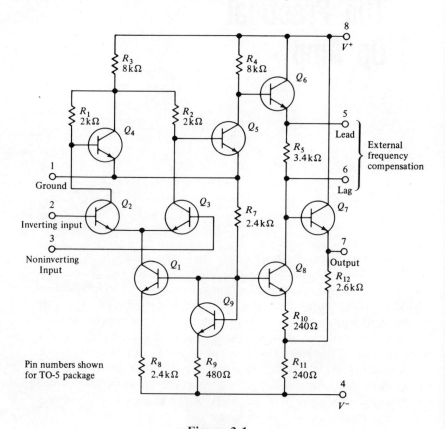

Figure 3-1

Equivalent Circuit of *IC* Op Amp (Courtesy of Fairchild)

on a single silicon chip (which means it is a monolithic or *IC*, not a hybrid) and is intended for use as an operational amplifier at frequencies from dc to 30 MHz. Figure 3-1 indicates that the unit is a multistage transistor amplifier composed of the equivalent of 9 transistors and 12 resistors. We shall not attempt an analysis of this circuit because this is a problem for the manufacturer, not for us. We are concerned only with the *overall* behavior of the device, not with the values of the currents and voltages developed within it. Note that there are 8 terminals extending from the diagram. These correspond to the leads which protrude from the case. The terminals are numbered and labeled as follows:

1 GROUND
2 INVERTING INPUT
3 NONINVERTING INPUT
4 V^-
5 LEAD
6 LAG
7 OUTPUT
8 V^+

We shall now examine each of these terminals individually.

1 **Ground**   The ground terminal is a common reference point for both input and output voltages. In other words, input voltages are applied between one or both of the *in*put terminals and ground, and the output voltage is generated between the *out*put terminal and ground.

2 **Inverting input**   The inverting input terminal is one of *two* input terminals to the op amp. It is called the "inverting" input terminal because input voltages applied to this terminal will be inverted in the output. To learn what we mean by inverted, we must read on. Figure 3-2(a) shows the waveform of a sinusoidal voltage, V_2. Suppose this voltage is applied between the inverting input terminal and ground, with the *non*inverting input terminal (3) connected to ground (we shall elaborate on this point later). The output voltage, V_o, generated between the output terminal and ground will be amplified, but will be *180 degrees out of phase* with the input voltage, V_2. The waveform of V_o is shown in Figure 3-2(b). Note in Figure 3-2(a) and Figure 3-2(b) that when V_2 is positive-going, V_o is negative-going, and vice versa. In other words, when the input voltage is applied between the inverting input terminal and ground, the op amp will both amplify *and* invert the polarity of the input signal.

3 **Noninverting input**   The noninverting input terminal is the second of the two input terminals to the op amp. It should appear obvious that this terminal will produce the opposite effect from the inverting input terminal. Suppose sinusoidal voltage, V_3, is applied between the noninverting input terminal and ground, with the inverting input terminal (2) connected to ground; the waveform of V_3 is shown in Figure 3-2(c). The output voltage will be amplified and *in phase*

with the input voltage, as shown in Figure 3-2(d). In other words, when the input voltage is applied between the noninverting input terminal and ground, the op amp will amplify the input but will *not* invert the polarity.

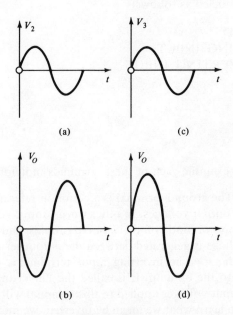

(a)   (c)

(b)   (d)

Figure 3-2

(a) Waveform of Voltage at Inverting Input; (b) Waveform of Output Voltage; (c) Waveform of Voltage at Noninverting Input; (d) Waveform of Output Voltage

4 V^- The V^- terminal is provided for the connection of a dc power supply to the op amp. It is necessary that the negative terminal of the supply be connected to the V^- terminal of the op amp while the positive terminal of the supply is connected to ground. All electronic amplifiers must be powered by dc supplies or batteries in order to operate.

5 **Lead**   and   6 **Lag**   The lead and lag terminals are provided for external frequency or phase compensation. The function of these terminals will be discussed in detail in a later chapter.

7 **Output**   The output terminal is the point at which the output voltage of the op amp is generated. The output voltage, V_O, is developed between the output terminal and ground.

8 V^+ The V^+ terminal is provided for the connection of a second dc power supply to the op amp. It is necessary that the positive terminal

of this supply be connected to the V^+ terminal of the op amp while the negative terminal of the supply is connected to ground. In order that the op amp be capable of functioning as a dc as well as an ac amplifier, it is essential that two dc power supplies be provided. We shall elaborate on this point later.

Figure 3-3 shows the standard triangular symbol which is used to represent the op amp schematically. Note the eight leads protruding from the symbol.

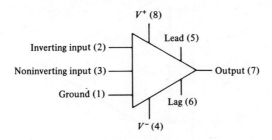

Figure 3-3

Wiring Diagram for Op Amp

The representation of Figure 3-3 is a wiring diagram supplied by the op amp manufacturer. This diagram enables the engineer or technician to connect the external circuitry (input, output, supplies, and so on) to the proper terminals of the op amp. Figure 3-4 shows a simpler schematic which is

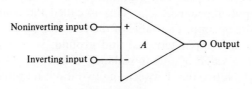

Figure 3-4

Schematic Diagram of Op Amp

used to represent the op amp in circuit diagrams. Note that the terminals for the power supplies, ground, and lead and lag have been omitted for simplicity. The non inverting input terminal is indicated by a "plus" sign and the inverting input terminal is indicated by a "minus" sign (the minus sign symbolizes the inversion). The letter "A" on the triangular symbol is an indication of the fact that the symbol represents an amplifier.

3-2   The Black Box Equivalent

At last all of the work involved in Chapter 2 will now pay off as we set out to examine the black box equivalent of the practical op amp. Let us begin by studying the input circuit of the op amp. Note in Figure 3-5 that there

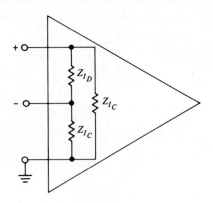

Figure 3-5

Equivalent Input Circuit of Op Amp

are actually *three* input terminals. These are the noninverting input terminal (marked plus), the inverting input terminal (marked minus), and ground. Now let us move "inside" the box. Notice that between each input terminal and ground (between plus and ground, and between minus and ground) there is an input impedance, Z_{IC}. This is called the *common-mode input impedance* of the op amp. The value of the common-mode input impedance seen between either input terminal and ground, is roughly the same for both inputs. The value of this impedance is extremely high, generally in excess of 1 MΩ. Notice that between the two input terminals (between plus and minus) there is another input impedance, Z_{ID}. This is called the *differential input impedance of the op amp.* The value of this impedance, although high, is not quite as high as that of the common-mode input impedance, Z_{IC}. The value of Z_{ID} generally runs from 10 kΩ to 100 kΩ or higher, depending upon the type of op amp. Summarizing, we write

Z_{IC} = the common-mode input impedance of the op amp,

Z_{ID} = the differential input impedance of the op amp.

Thus, Figure 3-5 represents the black box equivalent of the input circuit of the op amp. Note that the circuit is represented by *three* separate impedances. Does this mean that these three impedances are actually connected inside the op amp? Obviously not, since we have already seen in Figure 3-1 that the internal circuitry of the op amp is composed of the complex interconnection of a number of transistor amplifier stages. However, as far as we are concerned, the circuit will be treated as though these impedances are actually connected inside the box.

The practical op amp is designed so that *two* input voltages can be applied to its input terminals simultaneously, as shown in Figure 3-6. Input voltage V_{I_1} is applied between the *plus* input terminal and ground, and input voltage V_{I_2} is applied between the *minus* input terminal and ground. These voltages are defined as follows:

V_{I_1} = voltage at the plus terminal with respect to ground,

V_{I_2} = voltage at the minus terminal with respect to ground.

The op amp is designed to amplify the algebraic *difference* between the two input voltages. In other words, the amplifier will generate an output voltage directly proportional to the difference between these two voltages. Thus, the op amp is essentially a *differential* amplifier. The ability to amplify the difference between the two input voltages yields considerable flexibility to the op amp as we shall see later. Let us redefine this *difference* voltage, $V_{I_1} - V_{I_2}$, as V_I. Thus, we write

$$V_{I_1} - V_{I_2} = V_I = \textbf{the difference voltage.} \qquad \textbf{(3-1)}$$

Notice in Figure 3-6 that the difference voltage is developed across the differential input impedance, Z_{ID}.

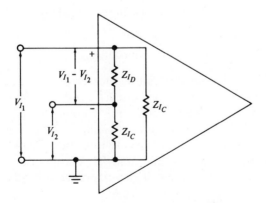

Figure 3-6

Amplification of the Difference Voltage

Figure 3-7 shows the complete black box equivalent circuit of the op amp. Note that the controlled voltage generator, AV_I, is directly proportional to the difference voltage, V_I. In other words, the op amp amplifies the *difference* between the two input voltages, *not* the input voltages themselves. The

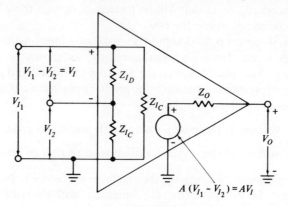

Figure 3-7

Complete Equivalent Circuit of Op Amp

value of the op amp gain, A, generally runs from 1000 to 10,000, or higher, while the value of Z_O is in the neighborhood of 50 Ω to a few hundred ohms. Figure 3-7 indicates that the performance of the op amp depends upon the values of *four* parameters. These are

$$Z_{IC} = \text{the common-mode input impedance}$$
$$Z_{ID} = \text{the differential input impedance}$$
$$A = \text{the voltage gain}$$
$$Z_O = \text{the output impedance.}$$

The values of these parameters can be measured by various experimental techniques. However, we shall not discuss these techniques at this point.

It was mentioned previously that the output voltage is proportional to the *algebraic* difference between the two input voltages. This means that the polarity of the output voltage depends upon the polarity of the difference voltage. Therefore, in order to determine the polarity of the output voltage, we must first know the polarity of the difference voltage. To do this, we subtract input voltage V_{I_2} *algebraically* from input voltage V_{I_1}. If the difference voltage, V_I, is a positive number, the potential at the output terminal is positive with respect to ground; if V_I is negative, the potential at the output terminal is negative with respect to ground. Finally, if the two input voltages are *equal* (in magnitude and phase), both V_I and V_O are equal to zero. We shall illustrate these concepts shortly, using specific examples. We now summarize the previous points as follows:

If polarity of V_I is positive: Polarity of V_O is positive.

If polarity of V_I is negative: Polarity of V_O is negative.

If $V_{I_1} = V_{I_2}$: V_O = zero.

We shall now present a graphical means of viewing the op amp operation. The purpose of this approach is twofold: First, it explains some of the previously discussed concepts by giving the reader a slightly different viewpoint, and second, it illustrates clearly the principle of saturation. Figure 3-8 shows a graph of output voltage, V_O, plotted against input

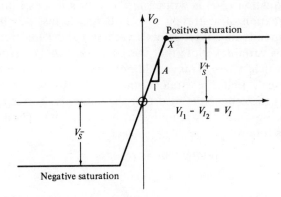

Figure 3-8

Voltage Transfer Characteristic

difference voltage, V_I. A curve of this type is called a *voltage transfer characteristic*. In the following discussion, we shall assume for simplicity that the value of the load impedance, Z_L, is much greater than the value of the output impedance, Z_O. If this is true, we can say that the value of the output voltage, V_O, is approximately equal to the value of the controlled voltage generator, AV_I. This can be expressed as follows:

$$\text{For } Z_L \gg Z_O: \quad V_O \simeq AV_I. \tag{3-2}$$

Reference to Figure 3-8 reveals that in the vicinity of the origin (for small values of V_I), the curve is a straight line passing through the origin and having a steep, positive slope. The reader learned in elementary algebra that the equation of a straight line can always be written in the following form:

$$y = mx + b. \tag{3-3}$$

In this equation, y is the dependent variable (plotted on the vertical axis), x is the independent variable (plotted on the horizontal axis), m is the slope, and b is the y-intercept. In the vicinity of the origin, the curve of Figure 3-8 is a straight line. However, V_O (instead of y) is plotted on the vertical axis and V_I (instead of x) is plotted on the horizontal axis. We also know from the previous discussion that $V_O = AV_I$. Using this information, we can write Equations (3-2) and (3-3), one above the other, as follows:

$$V_O = AV_I + 0. \tag{3-2}$$

$$y = mx + b. \tag{3-3}$$

Notice that Equation (3-2) is written in the same form as Equation (3-3), namely the equation of a straight line. Equating terms, we already know that V_O corresponds to y (vertical axis variable) and V_I corresponds to x (horizontal axis variable). Note that the y-intercept, b, corresponds to the V_O-intercept, which is *zero*. This should not be surprising since reference to Figure 3-8 reveals that the straight line passes through the origin (y-intercept equal to zero). Note also that the slope, m, corresponds to the *gain*, A, of the op amp; this is indicated in Figure 3-8. These results are summarized as follows:

$$b = V_O\text{-intercept} = \text{zero}, \tag{3-4}$$

$$m = \text{slope} = A \text{ (gain of the op amp)}. \tag{3-5}$$

The steeply sloped, linear portion of the graph of Figure 3-8 indicates that, in the vicinity of the origin, the output voltage is directly proportional to the input difference voltage. Thus, this graphical approach merely reaffirms what we already know to be true. If the graph of Figure 3-8 were drawn exactly to scale, the slope would be considerably steeper (almost vertical) because of the large values of gain exhibited by modern op amps. The *positive* slope of the graph illustrates a concept recently discussed, namely that of polarity. Note in Figure 3-8 that when V_I is positive V_O is positive (first quadrant), and when V_I is negative V_O is negative (third quadrant).

The direct proportionality relationship between V_O and V_I seems to imply that *any* value of V_I applied to the input will be multiplied by A in the output. This, however, is *not* the case. Reference to Figure 3-8 reveals that the graph is a straight, steeply sloped line *only up to point X* in the first quadrant. Beyond this point, the graph becomes a straight horizontal line; a similar situation prevails in the third quadrant. What does this mean?

It means that the output voltage is directly proportional to the input difference voltage only up to a certain point. Beyond this point, the output voltage can increase no more. In other words, every op amp has a particular value of maximum output voltage which it can generate. Even though the value of V_I is increased beyond point X, the value of V_O will not increase above this maximum voltage. Beyond point X, we say that the op amp is *saturated*. Just as a damp rag becomes saturated when it can no longer hold additional moisture, so does the op amp become saturated when its output voltage can no longer increase. Notice in Figure 3-8 that the op amp saturates for both positive and negative output voltages. In other words, there is a positive saturation voltage, $V_S{}^+$, and a negative saturation voltage, $V_S{}^-$. These definitions are summarized as follows:

$$V_S{}^+ = \text{the positive saturation voltage,}$$

$$V_S{}^- = \text{the negative saturation voltage.}$$

The values of $V_S{}^+$ and $V_S{}^-$ for any given op amp depend upon, and are slightly smaller than the values of the dc power supply voltages, V^+ and V^-. In order to increase the values of the saturation voltages, it is first necessary to increase the values of V^+ and V^-. However, the values of V^+ and V^- cannot be increased arbitrarily because each op amp has a maximum voltage rating which, if exceeded, can result in permanent damage to the device. The important point to bear in mind is that the op amp will saturate at some finite value of output voltage, and thus, there is a limit beyond which it will no longer provide an output voltage directly proportional to the input voltage.

Op amps are extremely versatile devices, having the ability to amplify both ac *and* dc voltages. We shall now illustrate some of the principles discussed in this section by means of specific examples.

EXAMPLE 3-1

The following values are given for the parameters and voltages of the circuit of Figure 3-7:

$A = 1000$ $V_{I_1} = +2$ mV (plus terminal positive with respect to ground)

$Z_O = 0$ $V_{I_2} = +1$ mV

$V_S{}^+ = +10$ V   These inputs are dc voltages.

$V_S{}^- = -10$ V

Compute the value of the output voltage, V_O.

Solution

Since $Z_O = 0$, we can say that $V_O = AV_I$. We can solve for the value of the output voltage by substituting into the equation, as follows:

$$V_O = AV_I = A(V_{I_1} - V_{I_2}),$$
$$V_O = 1000 \, [+2 \, \text{mV} - (+1 \, \text{mV})] = 1000 \, (+1 \, \text{mV}),$$
$$V_O = +1 \, \text{V}.$$

Note that the output voltage is directly proportional to the algebraic difference between the two input voltages. The plus sign in the answer for the output voltage indicates that the potential at the output terminal is positive with respect to ground.

EXAMPLE 3-2

Repeat Example 3-1 if V_{I_2} is changed to $+5$ mV.

Solution

Note that the potential at the minus terminal $(+5 \, \text{mV})$ is more positive than that at the plus terminal $(+2 \, \text{mV})$. This means that the difference voltage will be *negative*, resulting in a negative output voltage. Substituting into the equation, we get

$$V_O = A(V_{I_1} - V_{I_2}) = 1000 \, [+2 \, \text{mV} - (+5 \, \text{mV})],$$
$$V_O = 1000 \, (-3 \, \text{mV}) = -3 \, \text{V}.$$

The minus sign in the answer for the output voltage indicates that the potential at the output terminal is negative with respect to ground.

EXAMPLE 3-3

Repeat Example 3-1 if $V_{I_1} = V_{I_2} = +7$ mV.

Solution

Since both plus and minus input terminals are at the same positive potential with respect to ground, the value of the ouptut voltage will be equal to zero, as shown:

$$V_O = A(V_{I_1} - V_{I_2}) = 1000 \, [+7 \, \text{mV} - (+7 \, \text{mV})],$$
$$V_O = 1000 \, (0) = 0 \, \text{V}.$$

EXAMPLE 3-4

Repeat Example 3-1 if $V_{I_1} = +7$ mV and $V_{I_2} = -7$ mV (minus terminal negative with respect to ground).

Solution

Substituting into the equation, we get

$$V_O = A(V_{I_1} - V_{I_2}) = 1000 \,[+7 \,\text{mV} - (-7 \,\text{mV})],$$

$$V_O = 1000 \,(+14 \,\text{mV}) = 14 \,\text{V}.$$

Now, we must be very careful at this point. Note that the equation *predicts* that the output voltage, V_O, is equal to $+14$ V. The word "predicts" is used here because the equation is applicable only when the op amp is operating in its linear (nonsaturated) region. Recall from Example 3-1 that the value of the positive saturation voltage, V_S^+, is equal to $+10$ V for this particular op amp. Therefore, although the equation tells us that the value of V_O is $+14$ V, the actual value of V_O is only $+10$ V because the op amp saturates at this value. In other words, the output voltage "tries" to reach $+14$ V, but cannot increase above $+10$ V.

EXAMPLE 3-5

Repeat Example 3-1 if V_{I_1} and V_{I_2} are the ac sinusoidal waveforms shown in Figure 3-9(a) and Figure 3-9(b), respectively.

Solution

We use essentially the same procedure in solving ac problems as we did with dc. If the waveform of V_{I_2} is subtracted algebraically from that of V_{I_1}, the resulting difference waveform of V_I is shown in Figure 3-9(c). When the waveform of V_I is multiplied by 1000, the waveform of the output voltage will appear as shown in Figure 3-9(d).

EXAMPLE 3-6

Repeat Example 3-1 if the waveforms of V_{I_1} and V_{I_2} are the ones shown in Figure 3-9(e) and Figure 3-9(f), respectively.

Solution

When the waveform of V_{I_2} is subtracted algebraically from that of V_{I_1}, the resulting waveform of V_I will appear as shown in Figure 3-9(g). Note that the waveform of V_I has a peak value of 20 mV. To obtain the waveform of V_O, we must multiply the waveform of V_I by 1000. Thus, the equations predict that the waveform of V_O will be a sinusoid with a peak value of 20 V. However, we know that the op amp saturates at 10 V. Therefore, instead of the 20 V peak sinusoid predicted by the equations,

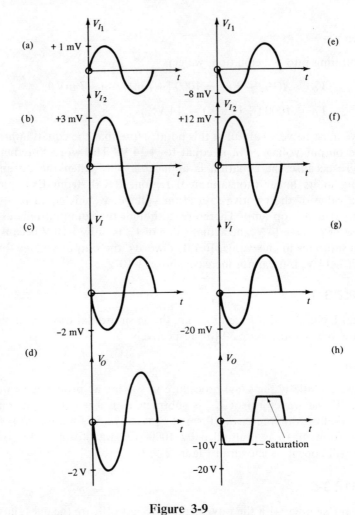

Figure 3-9

Waveforms for Examples 3-5 and 3-6

the actual waveform of V_O will be the *clipped* waveform shown in Figure 3-9(h). Note that the output voltage tries to reach 20 V, but cannot increase above 10 V due to saturation of the op amp.

Now, here is an important point. The function of an amplifier is not only to increase the size of the input voltage, but also to *retain the same wave-shape*. This is certainly *not* the case in Example 3-6. The waveform of the output voltage is not a sinusoid and is thus *distorted*, or twisted out of shape. Thus, the amplifier is not being used properly in Example 3-6.

3-3   The Common-Mode Rejection Ratio

A confession must be made at this point. We have not been completely honest with the reader. It was stated in the last section that the output voltage, V_O, is directly proportional to the input difference voltage, V_I. This implies that the output voltage will be equal to zero when the two input voltages are equal in magnitude and phase, that is, when $V_{I_1} = V_{I_2}$ (see Example 3-3). This, however, is *not* strictly true, but the situation is not as bad as it seems.

The two input terminals (plus and minus) are connected to two transistor amplifier stages within the interior of the op amp (see Figure 3-1). The output voltage will be directly proportional to the input difference voltage only when these two stages are exactly identical in every detail; that is, the two stages must be perfectly *balanced*. However, perfect balance is an impossibility when mass production manufacturing techniques are employed. Thus, every op amp has some degree of imbalance in its input circuitry. As a result of this imbalance, the output voltage is *not* directly proportional to the input difference voltage. In other words, the output voltage will *not* be equal to zero when $V_{I_1} = V_{I_2}$.

Now, let us examine the situation more closely. It can be shown that, due to the imbalance in the input circuitry of the op amp, the expression for the output voltage can be written as follows:

$$V_O = A_D(V_{I_1} - V_{I_2}) + M(V_{I_1} + V_{I_2}). \qquad (3\text{-}6)$$

$$\underset{\text{Difference}}{\uparrow} \qquad\qquad \underset{\text{Sum}}{\uparrow}$$

Note that the output voltage is equal to the sum of two terms. The first term is directly proportional to the *difference* between the two input voltages and the second is directly proportional to their *sum*. The first term, $A_D(V_{I_1} - V_{I_2})$, is called the *difference term*. A_D is referred to as the *differential gain* of the op amp. The second term, $M(V_{I_1} + V_{I_2})$, is called the *sum term*. For the moment we shall consider M to be merely a constant of proportionality. In other words, M has a specific value whose effect on the op amp operation will be studied shortly. We summarize these definitions as follows:

A_D = the differential gain of the op amp,

M = a constant of proportionality.

Now, let us examine the case for which the two input voltages are equal, that is, for $V_{I_1} = V_{I_2}$. According to the discussion of the previous section, we should expect the value of the output voltage to be equal to zero for this situation. We shall now rewrite Equation (3-6), setting $V_{I_1} = V_{I_2}$:

$$V_O = A_D(V_{I_1} - V_{I_2}) + M(V_{I_1} + V_{I_2}),$$

$$V_O = A_D(V_{I_1} - V_{I_1}) + M(V_{I_1} + V_{I_1}),$$

$$V_O = \quad\quad 0 \quad\quad + 2MV_{I_1}.$$

Notice that even though $V_{I_1} = V_{I_2}$, the output voltage is *not* equal to zero. The difference term is equal to zero but the sum term is not. In other words, there is a finite (nonzero) value of output voltage even though the input difference voltage is zero.

If $V_{I_1} = V_{I_2}$, we can say that as far as the op amp is concerned, the *same* voltage is applied to both input terminals, even though V_{I_1} and V_{I_2} may be two different, but equal signals. Since the two inputs (plus and minus) have a common voltage, we call this voltage the *common-mode input voltage*. This situation is depicted in Figure 3-10. Note in the figure that

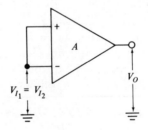

Figure 3-10

Common-Mode Input Voltage

both inputs are tied together so that $V_{I_1} = V_{I_2}$. We now define a new term known as the *common-mode* gain, A_C. The common-mode gain is the ratio of the output voltage to the common-mode input voltage. In other words, A_C is the gain of the op amp when the same voltage is applied to both input terminals.

$$A_C = \textbf{the common-mode gain} = \frac{V_O}{V_{I_1}} \quad \text{when} \quad V_{I_1} = V_{I_2}. \quad \textbf{(3-7)}$$

Applying a common-mode input voltage to the op amp is the same as saying that the input difference voltage is zero ($V_{I_1} = V_{I_2}$). We have already shown that when $V_{I_1} = V_{I_2}$, the output voltage, V_O, is equal to $2MV_{I_1}$. Thus, we can now compute the value of the common-mode gain as follows:

$$A_C = \frac{V_O}{V_{I_1}} \quad \text{when} \quad V_{I_1} = V_{I_2},$$

$$A_C = \frac{2MV_{I_1}}{V_{I_1}} = 2M,$$

$$A_C = 2M. \tag{3-8}$$

Thus, we have a relationship between the common-mode gain, A_C, and the constant of proportionality, M. We can now rewrite Equation (3-6) as follows, substituting for M:

$$V_O = A_D(V_{I_1} - V_{I_2}) + M(V_{I_1} + V_{I_2}), \tag{3-6}$$

$$V_O = A_D(V_{I_1} - V_{I_2}) + \frac{A_C}{2}(V_{I_1} + V_{I_2}). \tag{3-9}$$

Finally, we must define one more term called the *common-mode rejection ratio*, C. The common-mode rejection ratio is the ratio of the differential gain, A_D, to the common-mode gain, A_C:

$$C = \text{the common-mode rejection ratio} = \frac{A_D}{A_C}. \tag{3-10}$$

We can now rewrite Equation (3-9) as follows, substituting for A_C:

$$V_O = A_D(V_{I_1} - V_{I_2}) + \frac{A_C}{2}(V_{I_1} + V_{I_2}), \tag{3-9}$$

$$V_O = A_D(V_{I_1} - V_{I_2}) + \frac{A_D}{2C}(V_{I_1} + V_{I_2}). \tag{3-11}$$

$$\uparrow \qquad\qquad \uparrow$$
Difference   **Sum or error**

Now just what does all this seeming nonsense mean? Let us study Equation (3-11) in detail and find out. Note that the output voltage is again equal to the sum of two terms, a difference term and a sum (or error) term. For proper differential amplifier operation, we should like the output voltage to be directly proportional to the input difference voltage *only*. This means that the sum term must be equal to zero. In order for the sum term to be equal to zero, it is necessary that the value of the common-mode rejection ratio, C, be equal to infinity; this should be evident from an inspection of Equation (3-11). Under these *ideal* conditions, the gain, A, of the op amp will be the same as the differential gain, A_D. However, C will be equal to infinity only when the two input stages of the op amp are perfectly balanced. Since it is impossible to achieve perfect balance, C will never be infinite in practice, and thus the sum term will never be equal to zero. Therefore, the sum term represents an *error* in the value of the output voltage. In practice, we should like this sum (or error) term to be as small as possible. Thus, we should like the value of C to be as *large* as possible. How do we make the value of C very large? This again is a problem for the op amp manufacturer. All that we need know is that the larger the value of C, the smaller the error in the output voltage. We shall illustrate the effect of the common-mode rejection ratio in the following example:

EXAMPLE 3-7

The following parameters and voltages are given for an op amp circuit:

$$A_D = 1000 \qquad V_{I_1} = +2 \text{ mV dc}$$
$$C = 10,000 \qquad V_{I_2} = +1 \text{ mV dc.}$$

Compute the value of the output voltage, V_O.

Solution

The value of V_O can be computed by substituting the various values into Equation (3-11), as follows:

$$V_O = A_D(V_{I_1} - V_{I_2}) + \frac{A_D}{2C}(V_{I_1} + V_{I_2}),$$

$$V_O = 1000(+2 \text{ mV} - 1 \text{ mV}) + \frac{1000}{2(10,000)}(+2 \text{ mV} + 1 \text{ mV}),$$

$$V_O = 1 \text{ V} + 0.15 \text{ mV},$$

$$V_O = 1 \text{ V} + 0.00015 \text{ V} = 1.00015 \text{ V} \simeq 1 \text{ V.}$$
$$\qquad\quad \uparrow \qquad\qquad \uparrow$$
$$\qquad \textbf{Difference} \quad \textbf{Error}$$

Note that the value of the difference term, $+1$ V, is much larger than that of the error term, $+0.15$ mV. This is due to the relatively large value of C. In this example, the percentage error which results from an imbalance in the input stages of the op amp is 0.015 percent. This indicates very close matching of the two input stages. In future discussions in this text we shall assume, for simplicity, that the value of C is infinite. However, the reader should be aware of the fact that a finite (noninfinite) value of C results in a finite (nonzero) error.

3-4　Single-Input Applications

The modern op amp is an extremely versatile device. We have seen in previous sections that it can be used as a differential amplifier. It can also be used to amplify a *single-input* voltage. Suppose we have a voltage which we should like to amplify. Suppose also that we connect this voltage, V_{I_1}, between the plus and ground terminals of the op amp as shown in Figure 3-11. Next, we connect a wire from the minus terminal to ground as shown

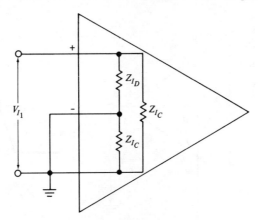

Figure 3-11

Minus Terminal Grounded

in the figure. This wire effectively shorts out the common-mode input impedance, Z_{IC}, between the minus terminal and ground. It also places the differential input impedance, Z_{ID}, in parallel with the *other* Z_{IC} (the one between the plus terminal and ground). Since the minus and ground terminals are now connected in common, there are effectively only *two* input terminals across which an input voltage may be connected. These are the plus terminal and the ground (or minus) terminal. Reference to Figure 3-11 reveals that the input impedance seen looking into these terminals is equal to the parallel equivalent of Z_{ID} and Z_{IC}. It was mentioned earlier in the chapter that the value of Z_{IC} is generally much larger than that of Z_{ID}. Thus, we can say that the value of the parallel equivalent is approximately equal to that of Z_{ID} alone. For ease of representation, we shall refer to Z_{ID} simply as Z_I from this point on in the text. Thus, when the minus terminal is connected to ground, the impedance seen looking into the input (plus and ground) terminals is approximately equal to Z_I (previously called Z_{ID}) as shown in Figure 3-12(a).

Since the minus terminal is connected to ground, V_{I_2} = zero. Therefore, we can write the following expression:

$$V_O = A(V_{I_1} - V_{I_2}) = A(V_{I_1} - 0) = AV_{I_1},$$

$V_O = AV_{I_1}$ when the minus terminal is connected to ground. (3-12)

A study of Equation (3-12) reveals that when the minus terminal is connected to ground, the output voltage will have the *same* polarity as (or be *in* phase with) the input voltage, V_{I_1}. It is for this reason that we call the

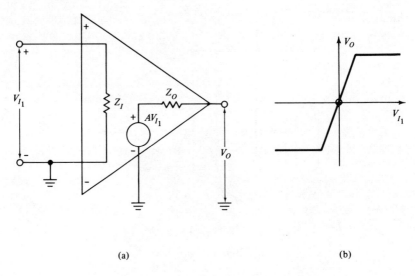

(a)   (b)

Figure 3-12

(a) Noninverting Amplifier; (b) Voltage Transfer Characteristic

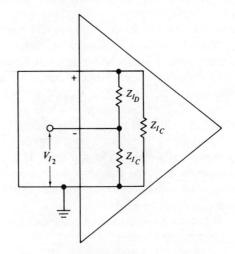

Figure 3-13

Plus Terminal Grounded

circuit of Figure 3-12(a) a *noninverting amplifier*. Note that the polarity of the controlled voltage generator, AV_{I_1}, is the *same* as that of the input voltage, V_{I_1}. This indicates that when the potential at the plus terminal is positive with respect to ground (V_{I_1} positive), the potential at the output terminal will also be positive with respect to ground (V_O positive), and vice versa. The positive slope of the voltage transfer characteristic shown in Figure 3-12(b) is a further indication of the nonreversal aspect of this particular circuit.

In Figure 3-13 a voltage, V_{I_2}, is connected between the minus and ground terminals while a wire is connected from the plus terminal to ground. This time the wire shorts out the Z_{IC} between the plus terminal and ground, placing Z_{ID} in parallel with the other Z_{IC} (the one between the minus terminal and ground). Since the plus and ground terminals are now in common, the two input terminals to the op amp are the minus terminal and the ground (or plus) terminal. The input impedance to the op amp is again equal to the parallel equivalent of Z_{ID} and Z_{IC}. As before, we can say that the input impedance is approximately equal to Z_I (previously called Z_{ID}) as shown in Figure 3-14(a).

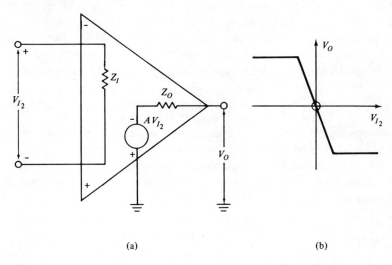

(a)   (b)

Figure 3-14

(a) Inverting Amplifier; (b) Voltage Transfer Characteristic

Since the plus terminal is connected to ground, V_{I_1} = zero. Therefore, we can write the following expression:

$$V_O = A(V_{I_1} - V_{I_2}) = A(0 - V_{I_2}) = -AV_{I_2},$$
$$V_O = -AV_{I_2} \text{ when the plus terminal is connected to ground. (3-13)}$$

A study of Equation (3-13) reveals that when the plus terminal is connected to ground, the output voltage will have the *opposite* polarity from (or be 180 degrees *out* of phase with) the input voltage, V_{I_2}. It is for this reason that we call the circuit of Figure 3-14(a) an *inverting amplifier*. Note that the polarity of the controlled voltage generator, AV_{I_2}, is *opposite* from that of the input voltage, V_{I_2}. This indicates that when the potential at the minus terminal is positive with respect to ground (V_{I_2} positive), the potential at the output terminal will be negative with respect to ground (V_O negative), and vice versa. The negative slope of the voltage transfer characteristic shown in Figure 3-14(b) is a further indication of the phase-reversal aspect of this particular circuit.

Now this is really quite good. The versatility of the modern op amp permits it to be used as a differential amplifier (two inputs), or as a noninverting or inverting amplifier (single input).

SUMMARY

1.   The modern op amp is designed so that two input voltages may be applied to its input terminals simultaneously. The output voltage is directly proportional to the algebraic difference between these two voltages.
2.   Each op amp has finite values of positive and negative saturation voltages, V_S^+ and V_S^-. The output voltage of the op amp cannot increase above these values.
3.   Due to imbalances in the input stages of the op amp, the output voltage of the unit is not equal to zero when a common-mode voltage is applied to the input. The magnitude of the error is inversely proportional to the value of the common-mode rejection ratio of the unit.
4.   The op amp can be used to amplify single-input voltages. The connection of one extra wire will convert the op amp to a noninverting or an inverting amplifier.

PROBLEMS

3-1.   The following values and parameters are given for an op amp circuit:

$$A = 5000 \qquad V_{I_1} = +5 \text{ mV dc}$$
$$Z_O = 0 \qquad V_{I_2} = +4 \text{ mV dc}$$
$$V_S^+ = +15 \text{ V}$$
$$V_S^- = -15 \text{ V}$$
$$C = \text{infinity}$$

Compute the value of the output voltage, V_O.

3-2.   Repeat Problem 3-1 if $V_{I_1} = -8\,\text{mV}$ and $V_{I_2} = -6\,\text{mV}$.

3-3.   Repeat Problem 3-1 if $V_{I_1} = -5\,\text{mV}$ and $V_{I_2} = +6\,\text{mV}$.

3-4.   Repeat Problem 3-1 if $V_{I_1} = 0\,\text{mV}$ and $V_{I_2} = -2\,\text{mV}$.

3.5.   If $V_{I_1} = +6\,\text{mV}$, what value of V_{I_2} will bring the op amp of Problem 3-1 to the point of positive saturation?

3-6.   Repeat Problem 3-5 for negative saturation.

3-7.   If $V_{I_2} = -2\,\text{mV}$, what value of V_{I_1} will bring the op amp of Problem 3-1 to the point of positive saturation?

3-8.   Repeat Problem 3-7 for negative saturation.

3-9.   The voltages whose waveforms are shown in Figure 3-15 are applied to the inputs of the op amp of Problem 3-1. Sketch the waveform of V_O.

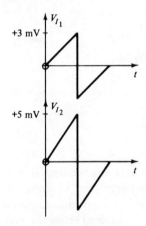

Figure 3-15

Waveforms for Problems 3-9 and 3-10

3-10.   Repeat Problem 3-9 if the peak value of V_{I_1} is changed to 1 mV and that of V_{I_2} is changed to 7 mV. Is the op amp functioning as an amplifier in this problem? Explain.

3-11.   (a) Repeat Problem 3-1 if $C = 10{,}000$.

(b) Compute the value of the percentage error in the output voltage resulting from the finite value of C.

3-12.   (a) Repeat Problem 3-1 if $C = 100{,}000$.

(b) Compute the value of the percentage error.

(c) What effect does the value of C have on the percentage error? Explain.

4

The Noninverting Amplifier

All modern aircraft are equipped with altimeters, devices that measure the distance between the airplane and the ground. Electronic circuitry within the airplane transmits a signal which is directed toward the ground. This signal is reflected from the ground and received by other circuitry within the airplane. The time required for the signal to travel to the ground and return to the aircraft is a measure of the distance between the airplane and the ground. An amplifier, which is located in the receiver, is used to boost the reflected signal in order to drive the altimeter indicator in the pilot's cockpit.The gain of this amplifier is carefully calibrated so that the indicator reads the correct distance. Suppose that the gain of the amplifier changes by a factor of two to one due to a large change in temperature. In this case the calibration is thrown off and the indicator no longer reads the correct distance. In other words, it is possible for the indicator to read 100 feet when the airplane is actually only 50 feet from the ground! This situation may cause the pilot some concern, to say the least. We have seen that a change in the gain of an amplifier due to environmental conditions can cause serious problems. Therefore, it is usually preferable that the gain of an amplifier remain constant, independent of these conditions. However, we shall see shortly that the gain of the op amp *does* vary considerably when the temperature changes. In this chapter we shall discuss techniques that are used to stabilize the gain of an amplifier.

4-1 Gain Variation

Although the modern op amp has a large value of gain, this gain is subject to a considerable amount of variation. The two major causes of gain variation are temperature and production yield. First, let us deal with the effect of temperature. It was mentioned earlier in the text that op amps are fabricated from semiconductor materials. Due to the temperature-sensitive nature of semiconductor materials, it is logical to expect that any device fabricated from these materials will exhibit behavior which is sensitive to temperature. The op amp is no exception. All of the quantities associated with the op amp (Z_I, Z_{Ic}, A, Z_O, C) vary with temperature. The quantity which has the greatest effect on the performance of the op amp, however, is the gain, A. A typical unit of the Fairchild μA702A has a gain of 3600 at room temperature ($+20°C$). However, the value of the gain varies from 4000 at $-40°C$ to 2600 at $+120°C$. This is quite a variation! It was mentioned earlier that the amplifier is frequently placed in environments where the temperature fluctuates considerably. Examples are airplanes, missiles, and space capsules. Thus, the temperature-sensitivity of its gain would seem, at first glance, to disqualify the op amp from use in these environments. However, it is precisely in these environments, where space is at a premium, that the op amp is most desirable because of its small size. We shall resolve this seeming paradox in the following section.

We shall now discuss the second cause of gain variation. Mass production techniques are such that it is impossible to fabricate large quantities of the same type of unit, such as the μA702A, with exactly matching characteristics. For example, it was mentioned that the value of gain at room temperature is equal to 3600 for a *typical* μA702A. However, due to production variations Fairchild specifies that the gain can be as low as 2500 and as high as 6000 at room temperature. This means that when you buy a μA702A op amp from the manufacturer, the gain of the unit can be anywhere between 2500 and 6000 at room temperature. In other words, you will not know the value of gain for your unit unless you measure it yourself. This uncertainty in the value of A is troublesome for a few reasons.

Large electronic systems generally contain quite a few amplifiers. If an electronics firm contracts to deliver a large number of systems to a buyer, the systems are manufactured on an assembly line basis after the design has been completed. If op amps are inserted into each of these systems without first having their gains measured, each system will function *differently* due to the different gains of the op amps. Under these conditions, the buyer will probably no longer do business with the electronics firm. We could, of course, measure the op amp gains before inserting the units into the systems. For example, suppose that the desired value of gain for one of the op amps in the system is 3600. We can assign an employee to measure the gains of the op amps which we have purchased, instructing him to select only those units whose gains are 3600. But, what do we do with the other units? Should we throw them away? This is obviously a very inefficient approach. We could ask the manufacturer to send us only those units whose gains are 3600. Then *he* would have to select the units, with the result that the price of each unit would become inordinately high.

Thus, we have seen that the gain of the op amp varies considerably. This poses a major design problem, a problem whose solution will be discussed in the following sections.

4-2   Negative Feedback

We have spent the better part of the past few chapters praising the modern op amp. Its many advantages include small size, low price, high reliability, and considerable versatility. However, the gain variation due to environmental conditions and mass production techniques seems to make the op amp unsuitable for many applications. However, do not be discouraged. We can use the op amp and maintain a stable gain if we introduce a modification in the basic circuit. The modification depends upon whether we desire a noninverting or an inverting amplifier. In this chapter we shall discuss the modifications necessary to obtain a stable gain in a noninverting amplifier.

Figure 4-1 shows an op amp connected in a particular circuit. Before proceeding with a description of the operation of this circuit, we shall point out a number of simplifications which were made:

1. Both common-mode impedances (Z_{Ic}) have been omitted from the circuit. The values of these impedances are so large in comparison with other impedances in the circuit that their effect can be considered negligible.
2. The output impedance, Z_O, has been omitted. Its value is so small in comparison with the other impedances that it can be neglected.
3. Finally, we shall assume that the value of the source impedance, Z_S, is equal to zero.

These simplifications will facilitate the following discussion. We shall deal with the effects of Z_{Ic}, Z_O, and Z_S later in the chapter.

Notice in Figure 4-1 that two resistors, R_1 and R_2, are connected across the output terminals of the op amp. These resistors comprise a voltage divider. A portion of the output voltage, namely the voltage across R_2,

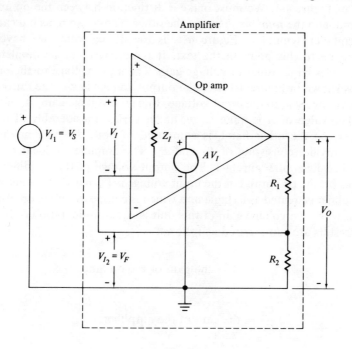

Figure 4-1

The Noninverting Feedback Amplifier

is *fed back* to the input of the op amp. It is for this reason that we call the circuit of Figure 4-1 a *feedback amplifier*. The voltage across R_2 is known as the *feedback voltage*, V_F. Since V_F is applied between the minus terminal of the op amp and ground, it is equal to V_{I_2} as shown in Figure 4-1. Similarly, the source voltage, V_S, is applied between the plus terminal and ground and is thus equal to V_{I_1}. These results are summarized as follows:

$$V_{I_1} = V_S = \text{the source voltage}$$

$$V_{I_2} = V_F = \text{the feedback voltage}$$

$$V_I = V_{I_1} - V_{I_2} = V_S - V_F = \text{the difference voltage.} \qquad (4\text{-}1)$$

Since the source is applied to the plus terminal of the op amp, the output voltage, V_O, will have the same polarity as V_S (see Figure 4-1). When the polarity of V_O is as shown in Figure 4-1, the polarity of V_F is indicated (minus terminal positive with respect to ground).

Before proceeding, it is necessary to describe an important aspect of the circuit of Figure 4-1. We must make a distinction between the op amp on one hand, and the *total amplifier* on the other. The op amp, as indicated by the triangular symbol in Figure 4-1, is the device which we have been studying up to this point in the text. It is purchased as a complete unit and provides large values of voltage gain. The input voltage to the op amp is V_I, as shown in Figure 4-1, and the output voltage is V_O. The ratio of the output voltage, V_O, to the input voltage, V_I, is the voltage gain, A, of the op amp. The value of A is quite large, but it varies considerably. The total amplifier, on the other hand, is composed of both the op amp *and* the resistive divider consisting of R_1 and R_2. The amplifier is located within the dashed lines of Figure 4-1. The output voltage of the amplifier is V_O (same as for the op amp), but the input voltage is V_S, *not* V_I. In other words, the amplifier is treated as a single unit which is composed of the op amp and the resistors. The voltage gain of this unit is equal to the ratio of V_O to V_S. These results are summarized as follows:

$$\frac{V_O}{V_I} = A = \text{the gain of the op amp,}$$

and

$$\frac{V_O}{V_S} = \text{the gain of the amplifier.}$$

We shall now present a qualitative discussion of the operation of the circuit of Figure 4-1. Recall that our goal is to maintain a stable gain. Concentrating now on the total amplifier, we should like the ratio of V_O to V_S to remain constant regardless of environmental conditions. Putting it another way, we should like to maintain a constant value of V_O for a given value of input, V_S. Suppose that the gain, A, of the op amp of Figure 4-1 increases due to a change in temperature. Since $V_O = AV_I$, an increase in A will cause an *increase* in the value of V_O. As a result of the voltage divider consisting of R_1 and R_2, an increase in V_O will cause an increase in V_F (see Figure 4-1). However, since $V_I = V_S - V_F$, an *increase* in V_F will cause a *decrease* in V_I, but a decrease in V_I will cause a *decrease* in the value of V_O. Thus, it appears as though V_O is increasing and decreasing at the same time, which is ridiculous. Let us explain what is happening. The increase in A *tends* to increase V_O. This increase in V_O is fed back to the input via R_2. The feedback is of such polarity as to decrease V_I. The decrease in V_I acts to decrease V_O, *thus offsetting the increase caused by the increase in the value of A.* Thus, the value of V_O, and hence the gain, tends to remain constant. The circuit of Figure 4-1 has the ability to adjust itself to correct for any changes brought about by environmental conditions.

We know that the output voltage, V_O, is directly proportional to both A (the gain of the op amp) and V_I (the input voltage to the op amp). In the previous discussion, the gain of the op amp *in*creased due to a change in temperature. There is nothing we can do about this. However, the feedback mechanism in the circuit of Figure 4-1 caused a *de*crease in the value of V_I, tending to keep V_O constant.

$$\overset{\text{Increase}}{\underset{\text{Decrease}}{\overset{\uparrow}{\underset{\downarrow}{V_O = A V_I.}}}}$$

Similarly, the feedback mechanism would cause an *increase* in V_I if the gain were to *de*crease.

If V_I were to decrease by the same ratio that A increases, the value of V_O would remain absolutely constant. In this case we say that the feedback amplifier provides *perfect correction.* However, no practical feedback amplifier can achieve perfect correction. In practice, there will always be *some* change in the value of V_O. How much *does* V_O change? How stable can we make the amplifier? What factors determine the amount of stability? These questions will be answered shortly.

The feedback amplifier of Figure 4-1 is an example of a *negative feedback system.* We use the word "negative" because the phase of the feedback is such as to *decrease* any change caused by external conditions. Negative feedback systems have a self-correcting ability, or a sort of built-in "intelligence." Negative feedback is a general concept which is used in all types of systems, both electrical and nonelectrical.

A sample negative feedback system is shown schematically in Figure 4-2.

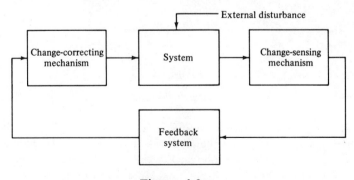

Figure 4-2

The Feedback System

In general, an external disturbance produces a change in a system. The system *senses* (or notices) the change by means of a change-sensing mechanism. The change-sensing mechanism transmits information concerning the change to the feedback system. The feedback system sends this information along to the change-correcting mechanism. The change-correcting mechanism *corrects* the system; that is, it tells the system what it must do in order to keep its performance constant. Comparing the system of Figure 4-2 with the circuit of Figure 4-1, we can make the following equations:

1. The *system* is the amplifier.
2. The *external disturbance* is the change in temperature.
3. The *change* is the increase in the op amp gain.
4. The *change-sensing mechanism* is the output voltage.
5. The *feedback system* is the voltage divider consisting of R_1 and R_2.
6. The *change-correcting mechanism* is the interconnection of V_S, V_F, and V_I.

It was mentioned before that in a negative feedback system, the *phase* of the feedback must be such as to *de*crease any change caused by external conditions. Figure 4-3 shows a circuit which is identical to that of Figure

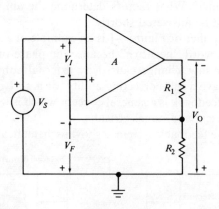

Figure 4-3

Positive Feedback

4-1 except for one point. The source voltage, V_S, is applied to the *minus* terminal of the op amp and the feedback is returned to the *plus* terminal. Therefore, both the output voltage, V_O, and the feedback voltage, V_F, will have the polarity shown in the figure. Now, suppose the gain, A, of the op amp increases due to a temperature change. This will cause an increase in the values of both V_O and V_F. Due to the polarity inversion, V_I is now equal to V_S *plus* V_F (instead of V_S *minus* V_F as in Figure 4-1). Thus, an increase in V_F will result in an *in*crease in the value of V_I (not a *de*crease as in Figure 4-1). This increase in V_I will cause a further increase in V_O, which will increase V_I still further, and so on. Thus, we see that the circuit of Figure 4-3 represents an *unstable system*. This is a *positive feedback system*. The word "positive" indicates that the phase of the feedback is such as to *increase* the change caused by external conditions. Thus, we must be careful to apply the feedback in the proper phase. We shall have more to say about positive feedback later.

4-3 The Closed Loop Gain

We shall now undertake a quantitative analysis of the feedback amplifier. The basic circuit of Figure 4-1 is shown again in Figure 4-4. Note that there are three currents indicated in the figure. I flows through the input imped-ance, Z_I, I_1 flows through R_1, and I_2 flows through R_2. It should be

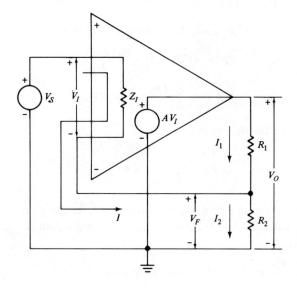

Figure 4-4

The Noninverting Feedback Amplifier

obvious from the figure that $I_2 = I + I_1$. The analysis of the circuit of Figure 4-4 is quite complex and involves a considerable amount of algebraic manipulation. We can, however, obtain a reasonably accurate result if we make one approximation. We shall assume that the value of the input impedance, Z_I, is approximately equal to infinity. If this is true, the current which flows through Z_I, I, is approximately equal to zero. This means that $I_2 = I_1$.

$$I_2 = I + I_1 = 0 + I_1 = I_1,$$

$$I_2 = I_1. \tag{4-2}$$

If $I_2 = I_1$, resistors R_1 and R_2 are in series. Thus, these resistors form a perfect voltage divider, enabling us to write the expression for V_F as follows:

$$V_F = \left(\frac{R_2}{R_1 + R_2}\right)V_O. \tag{4-3}$$

We know from previous discussions that the following relationships are valid:

$$V_O = AV_I,$$

$$V_I = V_S - V_F.$$

Thus, we can write the following:

$$V_O = AV_I = A(V_S - V_F) = AV_S - AV_F. \tag{4-4}$$

Substituting Equation (4-3) into Equation (4-4) we get

$$V_O = AV_S - A\left(\frac{R_2 V_O}{R_1 + R_2}\right), \tag{4-5}$$

$$V_O\left(1 + \frac{AR_2}{R_1 + R_2}\right) = AV_S. \tag{4-6}$$

Finally, we solve for the ratio V_O/V_S:

$$\frac{V_O}{V_S} = \frac{A}{1 + \dfrac{AR_2}{R_1 + R_2}}. \tag{4-7}$$

As mentioned in the last section, the ratio V_O/V_S is the gain of the total amplifier. We call this ratio the *closed loop gain*, or the gain of the amplifier *with feedback*, A_F:

$$\frac{V_O}{V_S} = A_F = \textbf{the closed loop gain.} \tag{4-8}$$

(gain of amplifier with feedback)

Thus, the expression for the gain of the amplifier of Figure 4-4 is given as follows:

$$A_F = \frac{A}{1 + A\dfrac{R_2}{R_1 + R_2}}. \tag{4-9}$$

Note that the gain of the amplifier is dependent upon both the gain of the op amp, A, and the resistive voltage divider composed of R_1 and R_2.

The circuit of Figure 4-4 is just *one* type of feedback amplifier. Electronics textbooks are filled with countless varieties of feedback amplifier circuits. However, regardless of the circuit configuration, the principles discussed in this chapter apply to all types of feedback systems. Since all feedback systems are similar in their operation, their behavior can be described in each case by a *general feedback equation*, as shown:

$$A_F = \frac{A_O}{1 + A_O\beta} \tag{4-10}$$

where: A_F = **the closed loop gain (gain *with* feedback)**

A_O = **the open loop gain (gain with*out* feedback)**

β = **the feedback factor.**

A comparison of Equation (4-9) with Equation (4-10) indicates that we can equate the following terms:

$$A_O = A, \tag{4-11}$$

$$\beta = \frac{R_2}{R_1 + R_2}. \tag{4-12}$$

Let us make one point clear before proceeding. Equation (4-10) is the *general* feedback equation. All negative feedback systems can be described by an equation in this form. Equation (4-11) and Equation (4-12), however, apply only to *one particular* feedback system, the circuit of Figure 4-4.

We shall now define one more term. The product of the open loop gain, A_O, and the feedback factor, β, is known as the *loop gain*, L.G.

$$A_O\beta = \text{L.G.} = \text{the loop gain.} \tag{4-13}$$

We shall soon see that the value of the loop gain is a measure of the stability of an amplifier.

Reference to Equation (4-10) reveals that the closed loop gain is equal to the open loop gain divided by one plus the loop gain. Suppose that the value of the loop gain is much greater than one. Then, we can write Equation (4-10) as follows:

$$A_F = \frac{A_O}{1 + A_O\beta} \simeq \frac{A_O}{A_O\beta} = \frac{1}{\beta}. \tag{4-14}$$

We call the term $1/\beta$ the *ideal closed loop gain.*

$$\frac{1}{\beta} = \text{the ideal closed loop gain.} \tag{4-15}$$

Now, here is an important point. Equation (4-14) states that if the value of the loop gain is much greater than one, the value of the closed loop gain is approximately equal to the reciprocal of the feedback factor. But, the feedback factor (and hence its reciprocal) depends only upon the resistive voltage divider, as shown by Equation (4-12). This means that the closed loop gain depends *only* upon the values of resistors R_1 and R_2 (which are relatively insensitive to temperature changes), and is thus *independent* of the op amp gain, A (which is highly temperature sensitive). Isn't this what we want? We now have an amplifier whose gain is relatively independent of environmental conditions. We shall now illustrate these concepts using specific examples.

EXAMPLE 4-1

An op amp has a gain, A, which varies from 2000 to 7000 over the operating temperature range for a particular environment. It is used in the circuit of Figure 4-4 with $R_1 = 200$ kΩ and $R_2 = 1$ kΩ. Compute the value of the closed loop gain at both temperature extremes.

Solution

Equation (4-11) tells us that the open loop gain, A_O, is equal to the op amp gain, A, for the circuit of Figure 4-4. Equation (4-12) gives the expression for the feedback factor. Let us first compute the value of the feedback factor:

$$\beta = \frac{R_2}{R_1 + R_2} = \frac{1 \text{ k}\Omega}{200 \text{ k}\Omega + 1 \text{ k}\Omega} \simeq 0.005.$$

We can now compute the value of the closed loop gain at both temperature extremes by substituting into Equation (4-10):

(a) For $A_O = A = 2000$:

$$A_F = \frac{A_O}{1 + A_O\beta} = \frac{2000}{1 + 2000(0.005)} = 182.$$

(b) For $A_O = A = 7000$:

$$A_F = \frac{A_O}{1 + A_O\beta} = \frac{7000}{1 + 7000(0.005)} = 194.$$

The results of this example are extremely important. Note that the gain of the op amp varies from 2000 to 7000, for a percentage change of 250 percent. As mentioned before, there is nothing that can be done about this. However, the closed loop gain or the gain of the *total* amplifier (op amp plus resistors) varies *only* from 182 to 194, for a percentage change of *only*

6.6 percent. Thus, the inclusion of negative feedback has added an enormous amount of stability to the amplifier circuit. Note, however, that the closed loop gain is *much smaller* than the op amp gain (182 and 194 compared with 2000 and 7000). Things did seem too good to be true. There is a price to be paid for everything good. In this case, *the price that must be paid for a stable gain is a reduction in the value of that gain.* This is the nature of negative feedback. We shall see shortly that we can improve the stability still further, but only at the price of a further reduction in the gain.

We can compute the value of the ideal closed loop gain as follows:

$$\frac{1}{\beta} = \frac{1}{0.005} = 200.$$

Note the close agreement between the value of the *ideal* closed loop gain (200) and the values of the *actual* gain (182 and 194). As mentioned previously, the actual gain approaches the ideal gain when the value of the loop gain is much greater than one. Computing the values of the loop gain in Example 4-1 we get:

(a)   For $A_O = A = 2000$:   L.G. $= A_O\beta = (2000)(0.005) = 10$.
(b)   For $A_O = A = 7000$:   L.G. $= A_O\beta = (7000)(0.005) = 35$.

Note that in both cases the value of the loop gain can be considered to be much greater than one. The larger the value of the loop gain, the more closely the actual gain approaches the ideal gain. We shall elaborate on this point shortly.

It is important to note that, although the incorporation of negative feedback added a considerable amount of stability to the circuit, it did *not* achieve a perfect correction. The gain of the feedback amplifier *did change* (from 182 to 194) with a change in temperature. Suppose that the value of the source voltage, V_S, is equal to 1 mV. Then the values of the output voltage at the temperature extremes would be:

(a)   For $A_O = A = 2000$: $V_O = A_F V_S = (182)(1 \text{ mV}) = 182 \text{ mV}$.
(b)   For $A_O = A = 7000$: $V_O = A_F V_S = (194)(1 \text{ mV}) = 194 \text{ mV}$.

It was mentioned earlier that in order to obtain a measure of stability, it is necessary that the input voltage to the op amp, V_I, change in such a manner as to *offset* any change in the op amp gain, A. We know that $V_O = AV_I$. Thus, we have enough information to compute the values of V_I at the temperature extremes:

(a)   For $A_O = A = 2000$:

$$V_I = \frac{V_O}{A} = \frac{182 \text{ mV}}{2000} = 91 \ \mu\text{V}.$$

(b) For $A_O = A = 7000$:

$$V_I = \frac{V_O}{A} = \frac{194 \text{ mV}}{7000} = 27.7 \; \mu\text{V}.$$

Now, here is a quantitative illustration of a concept discussed in the last section. The input voltage to the op amp, V_I, decreased (from 91 μV to 27.7 μV) to offset the *increase* (from 2000 to 7000) in the op amp gain. The gain increased from 2000 to 7000, for a ratio of 3.5 : 1. The input voltage decreased from 91 μV to 27.7 μV, for a ratio of 3.28 : 1. Note that V_I did *not* decrease in the same ratio as A increased, and thus, we did not obtain perfect correction. We shall illustrate the effect of the loop gain on the stability in the following example:

EXAMPLE 4-2

Repeat Example 4-1, except make $R_2 = 10$ kΩ.

Solution

First, we compute the new value of the feedback factor:

$$\beta = \frac{R_2}{R_1 + R_2} = \frac{10 \text{ k}\Omega}{200 \text{ k}\Omega + 10 \text{ k}\Omega} \simeq 0.05.$$

Next, we compute the values of the closed loop gain at the temperature extremes:

(a) For $A_O = A = 2000$:

$$A_F = \frac{A_O}{1 + A_O\beta} = \frac{2000}{1 + 2000(0.05)} = 19.8.$$

(b) For $A_O = A = 7000$:

$$A_F = \frac{A_O}{1 + A_O\beta} = \frac{7000}{1 + 7000(0.05)} = 19.95.$$

Note the extremely high stability of the gain of the feedback amplifier. The closed loop gain varies only from 19.8 to 19.95, for a percentage change of 0.76 percent. The results of Example 4-1 and Example 4-2 are summarized in Table 4-1. Note that the closed loop gain of Example 4-2 is considerably more stable than that of Example 4-1. Why is this so? The answer is that the values of loop gain for Example 4-2 (100 and 350) are *ten* times larger than those for Example 4-1 (10 and 35). Remember that the larger the value of the loop gain, the more closely the *actual* closed loop gain approaches the *ideal* closed loop gain, with a corresponding improvement in stability.

TABLE   4-1   COMPARISON OF FEEDBACK AMPLIFIERS

	Example 4-1	Example 4-2
Feedback factor	0.005	0.05
Actual closed loop gain	182 to 194	19.8 to 19.95
Percentage change in gain	6.6 percent	0.76 percent
Ideal closed loop gain	200	20
Loop gain	10 to 35	100 to 350

How did we achieve this increase in loop gain? We *in*creased the value of the feedback factor from 0.005 to 0.05 (a tenfold increase) by increasing the value of R_2 from 1 kΩ to 10 kΩ. Note, however, that this resulted in a *de*crease in the value of the ideal closed loop gain from 200 to 20 (a tenfold decrease). Thus, we see that the design of a feedback amplifier involves a compromise. The price to be paid for improved stability is a further decrease in the value of the closed loop gain. In general the required degree of stability for a particular amplifier depends upon the specifications of the system into which it is to be inserted. In other words, is it necessary that the pilot know the correct distance between his airplane and the ground to within 1 percent, or 5 percent, or 10 percent? These are some of the criteria that dictate the required degree of stability for a feedback amplifier.

The expression for the ideal closed loop gain can be rewritten as follows:

$$\frac{1}{\beta} = \frac{1}{\dfrac{R_2}{R_1 + R_2}} = \frac{R_1 + R_2}{R_2} = 1 + \frac{R_1}{R_2}. \tag{4-16}$$

This equation says that if the value of the loop gain is much greater than one, the value of the closed loop gain depends only on the ratio of the two divider resistors. Herein lies the beauty of the op amp. The device is manufactured and purchased as a single unit. The engineer or technician merely selects the appropriate values for resistors R_1 and R_2 and wires them into the circuit along with the op amp. This situation yields maximum flexibility for the engineer. It enables him to purchase a large quantity of a certain type of op amp for use in a particular electronic system. Since the closed loop gain is approximately independent of the op amp and depends only on the values of R_1 and R_2, the *same type* of op amp may be used in a variety of different feedback amplifier circuits.

It was assumed in the preceding discussion that the input impedance, Z_I, of the op amp was infinite. Strictly speaking, of course, we know that it is finite. Now, let us determine the effect of Z_I upon the performance of the feedback amplifier. Refer to Figure 4-5. The connection of a wire from

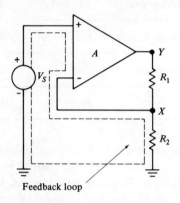

Feedback loop

Figure 4-5

The Feedback Loop

the resistive divider (point X) to the minus input terminal of the op amp forms a path known as the *feedback loop*, as shown in the figure. It is the feeding back of a portion of the output voltage to the input via this loop which is responsible for the phenomenon known as feedback. When the circuit is connected as shown in the figure, we say that the feedback loop is *closed*, and thus, the ratio of the output voltage, V_O, to the source voltage, V_S, is the *closed loop* gain, A_F, or the gain of the amplifier *with* feedback.

To determine the *open loop* gain, we proceed as follows: We disconnect the upper terminal of resistor R_1 from the output terminal (point Y in Figure 4-5) and connect it to ground, as shown in Figure 4-6. We say that the feedback loop is now *open*. Let us obtain an expression for the open loop gain. Notice in Figure 6-4 that Z_I and the parallel equivalent of R_1 and R_2 form a voltage divider at the input terminals of the op amp. Thus, we can write:

$$V_I = \frac{V_S Z_I}{Z_I + \dfrac{R_1 R_2}{R_1 + R_2}}. \tag{4-17}$$

The open loop gain is equal to the ratio of V_O to V_S with the feedback loop open. Thus, we write

$$A_O = \frac{V_O}{V_S} = \frac{AV_I}{V_S} = \frac{AV_S \dfrac{Z_I}{Z_I + \dfrac{R_1 R_2}{R_1 + R_2}}}{V_S}, \tag{4-18}$$

$$A_O = \frac{AZ_I}{Z_I + \dfrac{R_1 R_2}{R_1 + R_2}}. \tag{4-19}$$

Comparing Equation (4-19) with Equation (4-11), we see that when Z_I is finite, the *actual* open loop gain, A_O, is somewhat smaller than the op amp gain, A. Note, however, that A_O is directly proportional to A. If A doubles,

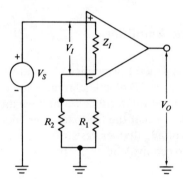

Figure 4-6

The Open Loop Circuit

A_O doubles, and so on. Thus, A_O suffers from the same variation as A. Therefore, the feedback loop must be closed in order to achieve stable operation.

Recall that we can achieve good stability by providing a large value of loop gain, $A_O\beta$. This can be accomplished by increasing the values of both A_O and β. If we *increase* β, however, we *decrease* the closed loop gain. How can we improve the stability of the amplifier while retaining the same value of closed loop gain? Obviously, we must maximize the value of A_O. Reference to Equation (4-19) reveals that this can be accomplished in a few ways. One way is to obtain an op amp with a large value of A. The second method concerns the voltage divider composed of Z_I and the parallel equivalent of R_1 and R_2 shown in Figure 4-6. A glance at Figure 4-6 and Equation (4-19) reveals that we should like the value of Z_I to be large compared with the value of the parallel equivalent of R_1 and R_2. This means that for a given value of Z_I, we should like the value of the parallel equivalent of R_1 and R_2 to be small. Recall from Equation (4-16) that the value of the ideal closed loop gain depends only upon the *ratio* of resistors R_1 and R_2, not the resistor values themselves. This means that we can obtain approximately the same value of ideal closed loop gain with $R_1 = 100\,\text{k}\Omega$ and $R_2 = 10\,\text{k}\Omega$ as with $R_1 = 10\,\text{k}\Omega$ and $R_2 = 1\,\text{k}\Omega$. In view of Equation (4-19) and our desire to maximize the value of A_O, it is preferable to select the *smaller*-valued set of resistors. What happens if we maximize A_O and still find it necessary to reduce the ideal closed loop gain in order to achieve good stability? In this case we simply connect a number of feedback amplifiers in cascade to make up the required overall gain.

4-4 The Feedback Amplifier

Having discussed the general principles of negative feedback, we turn to the treatment of the entire feedback amplifier as a single unit. In other words, we are going to put the feedback amplifier into a black box just as we did the op amp. Recall that the feedback amplifier is composed of both the op amp and the voltage divider resistors, R_1 and R_2. The first step in constructing a black box equivalent circuit for the amplifier is the determina-

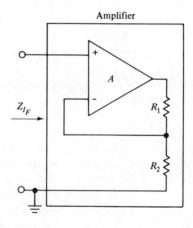

Figure 4-7

Schematic Diagram of Noninverting Feedback Amplifier

tion of the input impedance. We shall call this impedance the *closed loop input impedance*, or the input impedance of the amplifier *with feedback*, Z_{IF}:

$$Z_{IF} = \text{the closed loop input impedance.}$$

Figure 4-7 shows the entire feedback amplifier located within the confines of a *new* black box. Note that the input terminals to the amplifier are the plus terminal of the op amp and ground. The derivation of the expression for Z_{IF} is quite complex and involves a considerable amount of algebraic manipulation. The results of the derivation are shown in Figure 4-8(a).

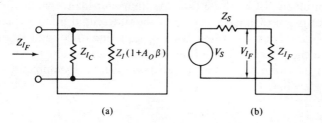

(a)   (b)

Figure 4-8

Closed Loop Input Impedance of Noninverting Feedback Amplifier

Note that Z_{IF} is equal to the parallel equivalent of two impedances. One is the common-mode input impedance of the op amp, Z_{Ic}, and the other is a term equal to the differential input impedance of the op amp, Z_I, multiplied by the factor, one plus the loop gain. Thus, we may write the following:

$$Z_{IF} = \frac{Z_{Ic}[Z_I(1 + A_O\beta)]}{Z_{Ic} + Z_I(1 + A_O\beta)}. \qquad (4\text{-}20)$$

In the last section, we assumed that the value of the source impedance, Z_S, was equal to zero. If this value is finite, however, the *actual* input voltage to the feedback amplifier, V_{IF}, will be less than the source voltage, V_S, due to the voltage divider action of Z_S and Z_{IF}. This situation is illustrated in Figure 4-8(b).

EXAMPLE 4-3

A feedback amplifier has the following values:

$$A_O = 2000$$
$$\beta = 0.005$$
$$Z_I = 100 \text{ k}\Omega$$
$$Z_{Ic} = 50 \text{ M}\Omega.$$

Compute the value of the closed loop input impedance, Z_{IF}.

Solution

To compute the value of Z_{IF}, we merely substitute into Equation (4-20).

$$Z_I(1 + A_O\beta) = 100 \text{ k}\Omega(1 + 10) \simeq 1 \text{ M}\Omega,$$

$$Z_{IF} = \frac{(1 \text{ M}\Omega)(50 \text{ M}\Omega)}{1 \text{ M}\Omega + 50 \text{ M}\Omega} \simeq 1 \text{ M}\Omega.$$

It was mentioned in Chapter 3 that the input impedance without feedback (open loop) is approximately equal to the differential input impedance of the op amp, Z_I. Thus, an examination of Equation (4-20) and Example 4-3 reveals that the incorporation of negative feedback results in a substantial increase in the input impedance (1 MΩ with feedback compared with 100 kΩ without feedback).

EXAMPLE 4-4

Repeat Example 4-3, except make $\beta = 0.05$.

Solution

$$Z_I(1 + A_O\beta) = 100 \text{ k}\Omega(1 + 100) \simeq 10 \text{ M}\Omega,$$

$$Z_{IF} = \frac{(10 \text{ M}\Omega)(50 \text{ M}\Omega)}{10 \text{ M}\Omega + 50 \text{ M}\Omega} = 8.3 \text{ M}\Omega.$$

The value of β in Example 4-4 was ten times larger than that of Example 4-3. This produced a tenfold increase in the value of the loop gain (from 10 to 100). The increased value of the loop gain resulted in a larger value of closed loop input impedance (8.3 MΩ compared with 1 MΩ). Therefore, in addition to improving the stability of the gain, an increase in the value of the loop gain increases the closed loop input impedance. There is, however, an upper limit to the value that can be attained for Z_{IF}. Figure 4-8(a) shows that Z_{IF} is equal to the parallel equivalent of Z_{IC} and another impedance. We know that the parallel equivalent of two impedances is always smaller than the smaller one. Thus, the value of the closed loop input impedance, Z_{IF}, can never be larger than that of the common-mode input impedance, Z_{IC}.

It can be shown that the expression for the *closed loop output impedance*, or the output impedance *with feedback*, Z_{OF}, is given as follows:

$$Z_{OF} = \frac{Z_O}{1 + A_O\beta}, \tag{4-21}$$

Z_{OF} = the closed loop output impedance.

In the last section, we assumed that the value of the output impedance, Z_O, was equal to zero. Since it is finite, however, the *actual* output voltage will be less than the controlled generator voltage due to the voltage divider action of Z_{OF} and Z_L. We shall return to this concept shortly.

EXAMPLE 4-5

Compute the value of Z_{OF} for the amplifier of Example 4-3 if $Z_O = 500 \, \Omega$.

Solution

We substitute into Equation (4-21) as follows:

$$Z_{OF} = \frac{Z_O}{1 + A_O\beta} = \frac{500}{1 + 10} \simeq 50 \, \Omega.$$

Thus, the incorporation of negative feedback results in a substantial decrease in the value of the output impedance.

We may now represent the black box equivalent circuit of the feedback amplifier as shown in Figure 4-9. Note that those parameters that depend

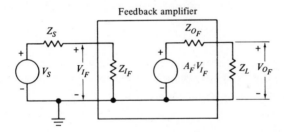

Figure 4-9

Equivalent Circuit of Noninverting Feedback Amplifier

upon the amplifier (Z_{IF}, A_F, and Z_{OF}) are located within the box. This circuit is in the same form as that used to represent the op amp (see Figure 2-8) with the exception that V_I, Z_I, A, Z_O, and V_O have been replaced by V_{IF}, Z_{IF}, A_F, Z_{OF}, and V_{OF}, respectively. The representation of Figure 4-9 is general and thus applies to all types of feedback amplifiers. However, the expressions given for Z_{IF} and Z_{OF} [Equation (4-20) and Equation (4-21)] apply only to one particular feedback amplifier, namely the noninverting amplifier of Figure 4-4. The polarities shown for V_S, A_FV_{IF}, and V_{OF} in Figure 4-9 indicate *no* polarity inversion.

The overall gain of the feedback amplifier (the ratio V_O/V_S) will, in general, be less than the closed loop gain, A_F. This is true for *two* reasons. First, the voltage divider at the input consisting of Z_S and Z_{IF} reduces the input signal so that the voltage at the input terminals of the amplifier is

V_{IF}, *not* V_S. Second, the voltage divider at the output consisting of Z_{OF} and Z_L reduces the output signal so that the voltage at the output terminals is V_{OF}, *not* $A_F V_{IF}$. Thus, to avoid a loss in the overall gain, we prefer that Z_{IF} be much larger than Z_S, and Z_{OF} be much smaller than Z_L. These inequalities are generally valid in practical situations as we shall see in the following example.

EXAMPLE 4-6

The following data are given for a noninverting feedback amplifier:

Op Amp	Feedback Network	Source	Load
$A = 5000$	$R_1 = 100 \text{ k}\Omega$	$V_S = 1 \text{ mV}$	$Z_L = 1 \text{ k}\Omega$
$Z_I = 50 \text{ k}\Omega$	$R_2 = 1 \text{ k}\Omega$	$Z_S = 1 \text{ k}\Omega$	
$Z_{Ic} = 10 \text{ M}\Omega$			
$Z_O = 200 \ \Omega$			

Compute the value of the output voltage of the feedback amplifier, V_{OF}.

Solution

To solve this problem we must work our way from the source to the load in Figure 4-9. It would seem sensible to begin with the computation of V_{IF}. However, we cannot compute the value of V_{IF} until we first know the value of Z_{IF}. To compute the value of Z_{IF}, we must first find the loop gain.

$$\beta = \frac{R_2}{R_1 + R_2} = \frac{1 \text{ k}\Omega}{100 \text{ k}\Omega + 1 \text{ k}\Omega} \simeq 0.01,$$

$$A_O = \frac{AZ_I}{Z_I + \dfrac{R_1 R_2}{R_1 + R_2}} = \frac{5000(50 \text{ k}\Omega)}{50 \text{ k}\Omega + (100 \text{ k}\Omega \| 1 \text{ k}\Omega)} \simeq 5000,$$

$$\text{L.G.} = A_O\beta = (5000)(0.01) = 50,$$

$$Z_I(1 + A_O\beta) = 50 \text{ k}\Omega(1 + 50) \simeq 2.5 \text{ M}\Omega,$$

$$Z_{IF} = \frac{(2.5 \text{ M}\Omega)(10 \text{ M}\Omega)}{2.5 \text{ M}\Omega + 10 \text{ M}\Omega} = 2 \text{ M}\Omega,$$

$$V_{IF} = \frac{V_S Z_{IF}}{Z_S + Z_{IF}} = \frac{(1 \text{ mV})(2 \text{ M}\Omega)}{1 \text{ k}\Omega + 2 \text{ M}\Omega} \simeq 1 \text{ mV}.$$

Thus, we see that since Z_{IF} (2 MΩ) is much larger than Z_S (1 kΩ), we can say that V_{IF} is approximately equal to V_S. To compute the value of the controlled generator voltage, $A_F V_{IF}$, we must first find the value of the closed loop gain, A_F.

$$A_F = \frac{A_O}{1 + A_O\beta} = \frac{5000}{1 + 50} \simeq 100.$$

Thus, the value of the controlled generator voltage is

$$A_F V_{IF} = 100(1 \text{ mV}) = 100 \text{ mV}.$$

Finally, before computing the value of the output voltage, we must find the value of Z_{OF}.

$$Z_{OF} = \frac{Z_O}{1 + A_O\beta} = \frac{200 \ \Omega}{1 + 50} \simeq 4 \ \Omega.$$

Thus, the output voltage is

$$V_{OF} = \frac{(A_F V_I)Z_L}{Z_{OF} + Z_L} = \frac{(100 \text{ mV})(1 \text{ k}\Omega)}{4 \ \Omega + 1 \text{ k}\Omega} \simeq 100 \text{ mV}.$$

Since Z_{OF} (4 Ω) is much smaller than Z_L (1 kΩ), we can say that V_{OF} is approximately equal to $A_F V_{IF}$.

Example 4-6 illustrates an important point. The value of Z_{IF} for a noninverting amplifier is so large and Z_{OF} so small, that the voltage dividers at both the input and output of the feedback amplifier have a negligible effect on the overall gain. Thus, we can say that the overall gain of the noninverting amplifier is approximately equal to the closed loop gain, A_F.

4-5 The Voltage Follower

There are applications in electronics where it is necessary to have a very large input impedance and a very small output impedance, Recall from the last section that the values of these impedances depend upon the value of the loop gain, We saw that an increase in the value of the loop gain increases the input impedance and decreases the output impedance. We know that the loop gain is directly proportional to the product of the open loop gain, A_O, and the feedback factor, β. The value of A_O is fixed for a given op amp, so the only way to increase the value of the loop gain is to increase the value of β, but this will decrease the value of the ideal closed loop gain. This is the price that must be paid for a large Z_{IF} and a small Z_{OF}.

The feedback factor, β, is actually the *fraction* of the output voltage which is fed back to the input. For example, an amplifier whose β is 0.05 feeds back 5 percent of the output voltage to the input. Therefore, if we want to increase β, we must feed back a larger percentage of the output voltage. Refer to Figure 4-10. Notice that a wire is connected from the output terminal directly to the minus terminal of the op amp. This means that all, or *100 percent* of the output voltage is fed back to the input. In other words, $\beta = 1$ for this circuit.

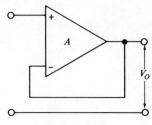

Figure 4-10

The Voltage Follower

Since the circuit of Figure 4-10 is nothing more than a special case of the general noninverting amplifier circuit, we can use Equation (4-10), Equation (4-20), and Equation (4-21) to obtain expressions for A_F, Z_{IF}, and Z_{OF}, respectively.

$$A_F = \frac{A_O}{1 + A_O\beta} = \frac{A_O}{1 + A_O} \simeq 1, \tag{4-22}$$

$$Z_{IF} = \frac{(Z_{Ic})[Z_I(1 + A_O\beta)]}{Z_{Ic} + Z_I(1 + A_O\beta)} \simeq \frac{(Z_{Ic})(A_O Z_I)}{Z_{Ic} + A_O Z_I}, \tag{4-23}$$

$$Z_{OF} = \frac{Z_O}{1 + A_O\beta} \simeq \frac{Z_O}{A_O}. \tag{4-24}$$

Note that the value of the closed loop gain is approximately equal to *unity*. This means that the value of the output voltage is approximately equal to to that of the input voltage. Since the input and output voltages are approximately equal, we say that the output *follows* the input, and thus the circuit of Figure 4-10 is known as a *voltage follower*. Those familiar with transistors and vacuum tubes will note that this circuit is similar to the emitter follower and cathode follower.

EXAMPLE 4-7

An op amp having the following parameters is connected as a voltage follower:

$$A = 5000$$
$$Z_I = 50 \text{ k}\Omega$$
$$Z_{Ic} = 10 \text{ M}\Omega$$
$$Z_O = 200 \text{ }\Omega.$$

Compute the values of A_F, Z_{IF}, and Z_{OF}.

Solution

To compute these values we merely substitute into Equation (4-22), Equation (4-23), and Equation (4-24).

$$A_F \simeq 1,$$

$$Z_{IF} = \frac{(Z_{Ic})(A_0 Z_I)}{Z_{Ic} + A_0 Z_I} = \frac{(10 \text{ M}\Omega)(250 \text{ M}\Omega)}{10 \text{ M}\Omega + 250 \text{ M}\Omega} \simeq 10 \text{ M}\Omega,$$

$$Z_{OF} = \frac{Z_O}{A_O} = \frac{200 \ \Omega}{5000} = 0.04 \ \Omega.$$

Note that the voltage follower has a closed loop gain of unity, a very high input impedance, and a very low output impedance. At this point you may well ask: What good is the voltage follower if it has a gain of unity? Since the output voltage is no larger than the input voltage, it seems as though the follower is useless as a voltage amplifier. The answer is that the follower is not an amplifier in the usual sense. It is used in applications where large input impedance and small output impedance are required. We shall have more to say about the follower later.

SUMMARY

1. The gain of the op amp varies both with temperature and production yield. This variation results in serious design problems.
2. The introduction of negative feedback stabilizes the gain, while positive feedback creates an unstable situation.
3. The closed loop gain of the feedback amplifier is more stable than the op amp gain, but it is also smaller.
4. The ideal closed loop gain depends only upon the feedback network, and is thus constant and independent of the op amp gain.
5. An increase in the value of the loop gain improves stability by making the closed loop gain closer to its ideal value.
6. The introduction of negative feedback in a noninverting amplifier increases the input impedance and decreases the output impedance.
7. The voltage follower has a gain of unity, a very high input impedance, and a very low output impedance.

PROBLEMS

4-1. The following data are given for a noninverting feedback amplifier:

Op Amp	Feedback Network
$A = 5000$ to $20,000$	$R_1 = 1 \text{ M}\Omega$
$Z_I = \text{infinity}$	$R_2 = 1 \text{ k}\Omega$
$Z_{Ic} = \text{infinity}$	
$Z_O = 0$	

(a) Compute the value of the closed loop gain at both temperature extremes.

(b) Compute the percentage change in the closed loop gain.

(c) Compute the value of the loop gain at both temperature extremes.

(d) Compute the value of the ideal closed loop gain.

4-2.   Repeat Problem 4-1, except make $R_1 = 100$ kΩ. Compare the results with those of Problem 4-1 and explain.

4-3.   Repeat Problem 4-1, except make $R_1 = 10$ kΩ. Compare the results with those of Problem 4-2 and explain.

4-4.   The source voltage, V_S, is -10 mV dc (plus terminal negative with respect to ground). Compute the values of the output voltage, V_O, at both temperature extremes for the amplifier of Problem 4-3. What is the polarity of V_O?

4-5.   Repeat Problem 4-4 for the amplifier of Problem 4-2.

4-6.   Repeat Problem 4-4 for the amplifier of Problem 4-1.

4-7.   Of the three amplifiers in Problem 4-1, Problem 4-2, and Problem 4-3, which is the most stable? Which is the least stable? Explain.

4-8.   The source voltage, V_S, applied to a noninverting amplifier is a sine wave whose peak value is 1 mV. The closed loop gain is 150.

(a) What is the peak value of the output voltage?

(b) What is the phase angle between V_S and V_O? Explain.

4-9.   The following data are given for a noninverting feedback amplifier:

Op Amp	Feedback Network
$A = 7000$ to $14,000$	$R_1 = 7$ MΩ
$Z_I = 30$ kΩ	$R_2 = 10$ kΩ
$Z_{Ic} = 15$ MΩ	
$Z_O = 100$ Ω	

Making use of Equation (4-19) for the open loop gain, A_O:

(a) Compute the values of A_O at both temperature extremes.

(b) Compute the values of A_F at both temperature extremes.

(c) Compute the value of the ideal closed loop gain.

4-10.   Repeat Problem 4-9, except make $R_1 = 700$ kΩ and $R_2 = 1$ kΩ.

(a) How do the values of closed loop gain compare with those of Problem 4-9?

(b) How does the value of ideal closed loop gain compare with that of Problem 4-9?

(c) Explain why we get identical values of ideal closed loop gain, but different values of actual closed loop gain using the *same* op amp.

4-11.   Compute the value of the closed loop input impedance in Problem 4-10.

4-12. Compute the value of the closed loop output impedance in Problem·
4-10.

4-13. The op amp of Problem 4-9 is used in a voltage follower.
(a) Compute the value of the closed loop gain.
(b) Compute the value of the closed loop input impedance.
(c) Compute the value of the closed loop output impedance.

4-14. An op amp has a gain which varies from 15,000 to 25,000. It is used in a feedback amplifier where $R_1 = 2$ MΩ and $R_2 = 2$ kΩ. It is specified that the closed loop gain is not to vary more than 2 percent of its minimum value. Does the feedback amplifier meet the specification?

4-15. If the amplifier of Problem 4-14 does not meet the specification, what should be done to improve the situation?

5

The Inverting Amplifier

In the last chapter we discussed the general principles of negative feedback, and then applied these principles to the analysis of a noninverting feedback amplifier. There are applications, however, where it is necessary that the output have a polarity opposite from that of the input. In this case, we must connect the op amp as an inverting amplifier. This chapter deals with the application of negative feedback to an inverting amplifier. We shall also illustrate the use of the voltage follower. Finally, we shall demonstrate the proper techniques used in applying negative feedback to a differential amplifier.

5-1 The Feedback Mechanism

Recall from Chapter 3 that the connection of a wire from the plus terminal of the op amp to ground results in the establishment of an inverting amplifier. The basic circuit is shown in Figure 5-1. Before proceeding with a discussion of this circuit, it should be mentioned that we shall again neglect the effects of Z_{Ic}, Z_O, and Z_S for the moment. We shall return to an analysis of these effects later in the chapter. Notice in the figure that the input voltage, V_{I_2}, is applied between the minus terminal of the op amp and ground. The polarity of the controlled voltage generator, AV_{I_2}, is an indication of the inversion of the signal. If the potential at the minus terminal is positive with respect to ground (V_{I_2} positive), the potential at the output terminal will be negative with respect to ground (V_O negative), and vice versa. Therefore, as in Chapter 3 we can write

$$V_O = -AV_{I_2}.$$

The voltage gain of the circuit of Figure 5-1 is equal to $-A$, the gain of the op amp (the minus sign indicates phase inversion). It was mentioned in the last chapter that A varies considerably. Thus, it is necessary to

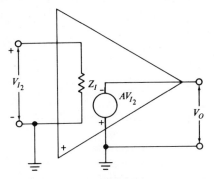

Figure 5-1

The Inverting Amplifier

introduce negative feedback into the circuit of Figure 5-1 in order to obtain some measure of stability.

It was shown in Chapter 4 that it is necessary to feed back the signal in the proper *phase*. In particular, it was demonstrated that the voltage divider technique used in the noninverting amplifier was unsatisfactory when applied to the inverting amplifier (see Figure 4-3). This situation led to a condition of *positive* feedback, a condition which promotes instability. Thus, it is necessary that we use a different technique to obtain negative feedback with the inverting amplifier. The basic circuit is shown in Figure 5-2. Note that the source voltage, V_S, is connected through a series resistor, R_1, to the input terminals (minus and ground) of the op amp. A second resistor, R_2, is connected from the output terminal (terminal B) to the minus terminal (terminal A). The polarities of V_S, V_{I_2}, and AV_{I_2} are shown in the figure. Of course, if the polarity of V_S were reversed, those of V_{I_2} and AV_{I_2} would also reverse.

With the polarity of V_S as shown in Figure 5-2, a current, I_1, will flow through R_1 in the direction shown. A second current, I_I, will flow into the op amp through input impedance Z_I. Due to the polarity inversion, the

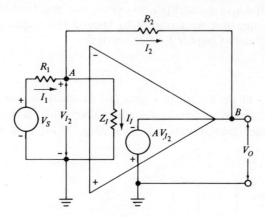

Figure 5-2

The Inverting Feedback Amplifier

output voltage, V_O, will be *negative*. This means that the potential at terminal B will be negative with respect to ground, and thus, it will also be negative with respect to the potential at terminal A. It follows that a current, I_2, will flow through R_2 from terminal A to terminal B (from high potential to low potential). Based on the previous discussion and the circuit of Figure 5-2, we can write some important equations. Applying Kirchhoff's current law, we can relate currents I_1, I_I, and I_2 as follows:

$$I_1 = I_I + I_2,$$

or

$$I_I = I_1 - I_2. \qquad (5\text{-}1)$$

Using Ohm's law, we can also write

$$V_{I_2} = I_I Z_I. \qquad (5\text{-}2)$$

We are now ready for a qualitative description of the feedback mechanism of the circuit of Figure 5-2. Suppose that the gain, A, of the op amp increases due to a change in the temperature. This tends to increase the output voltage, V_O. Due to the polarity inversion, the potential at terminal B will become *even more* negative with respect to that at terminal A. This means that the potential difference (or voltage drop) across R_2 will increase, resulting in a corresponding increase in the value of I_2. But Equation (5-1) shows that an increase in I_2 results in a decrease in I_I. Finally, Equation

(5-2) indicates that a decrease in I_1 results in a decrease in V_{I_2}. The decrease in V_{I_2} acts to *decrease* V_O, thus, offsetting any *increase* caused by the increase in the value of A. Similarly, it can be shown that V_{I_2} would *increase* to offset any change caused by a *decrease* in the value of A. Thus, the circuit of Figure 5-2 contains a negative feedback mechanism which consists primarily of resistor R_2. This resistor senses changes in the output and feeds back information concerning these changes to the input for correction.

5-2 The Miller Effect

We shall now undertake a quantitative analysis of the inverting amplifier. The circuit of Figure 5-2 is redrawn in Figure 5-3. Note the polarity of V_2, the voltage across R_2. Applying Kirchhoff's voltage law to the circuit, we can write the following equation:

$$-V_{I_2} + V_2 - AV_{I_2} = 0,$$

$$V_2 = V_{I_2} + AV_{I_2},$$

$$V_2 = V_{I_2}(1 + A). \tag{5-3}$$

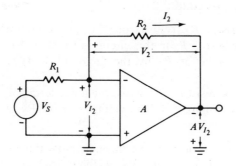

Figure 5-3

Analysis of the Inverting Feedback Amplifier

Using Ohm's law, we can write the expression for I_2 as follows:

$$I_2 = \frac{V_2}{R_2} = \frac{V_{I_2}(1 + A)}{R_2}. \tag{5-4}$$

Equation (5-4) merely provides an algebraic expression that can be used for the computation of the value of I_2. It says that we must divide the value of the voltage across the resistor, $V_{I_2}(1 + A)$, by the value of the resistance,

R_2. This is an elementary application of Ohm's law. Let us now divide both numerator and denominator of Equation (5-4) by the factor $(1 + A)$, as follows:

$$I_2 = \frac{V_{I_2}}{\dfrac{R_2}{(1 + A)}}. \qquad (5\text{-}5)$$

We know that when both numerator and denominator are divided by the same factor, the value of the fraction remains unchanged. Thus, Equation (5-5) may also be used to compute the value of I_2. Equation (5-5) states that the value of I_2 can be computed by dividing a *new* voltage, V_{I_2}, by a *new* resistance, $R_2/(1 + A)$. Let us call this new resistance R_2':

$$R_2' = \frac{R_2}{(1 + A)}. \qquad (5\text{-}6)$$

Thus, we can write the following:

$$I_2 = \frac{V_{I_2}}{R_2'}. \qquad (5\text{-}7)$$

The value of I_2 may be computed by the use of either Equation (5-4) or Equation (5-7).

Now here is an important point. Equation (5-4) and Equation (5-7) imply the following procedure:

(a) Remove resistor R_2 from its position in the circuit of Figure 5-3. The voltage across R_2 in this circuit is $V_{I_2}(1 + A)$.

(b) Divide the value of R_2 by the factor $(1 + A)$ to create a *new* resistor, R_2'.

(c) Place this new resistor, R_2', across the input terminals of the op amp as shown in Figure 5-4. The voltage across R_2' in this circuit is V_{I_2}.

Since the same value of I_2 flows through both the new resistor (R_2') and the old resistor (R_2), the circuits of Figure 5-3 and Figure 5-4 are *identical*. In other words, we may replace the circuit of Figure 5-3 with

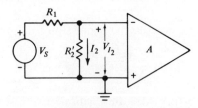

Figure 5-4

The Miller Resistance

that of Figure 5-4. It is important to mention that the preceding procedure may be used *only* as an analytical tool; that is, the procedure is to be applied only when solving problems using pencil and paper. It cannot be accomplished in the laboratory because the value of R_2' depends upon the value of the gain, and it is physically impossible to obtain a resistor which exhibits this property. In other words, R_2' is an *imaginary* resistor, not a real one.

Why do we go to the trouble of presenting this technique? The answer is twofold: First, it adds considerable insight into the operation of the inverting feedback amplifier. Second, it facilitates the analysis of this circuit, as we shall soon see. The technique is nothing more than a mathematical trick. It allows us to represent the inverting amplifier as shown in Figure 5-4 even though the *actual* physical circuit is the one in Figure 5-3. This technique is known as the *Miller Effect*. It finds applications throughout the enitre electronics field. It says that when an impedance is connected between the input and output terminals, it can be considered to be connected across the input terminals if its value is divided by the factor $(1 + A)$.

EXAMPLE 5-1

The following values are given for the circuit of Figure 5-3:

Op Amp	Feedback Network	Source
$A = 1000$	$R_1 = 1 \text{ k}\Omega$	$V_S = 1 \text{ V}$
$Z_I = 50 \text{ k}\Omega$	$R_2 = 10 \text{ k}\Omega$	

Compute the value of the output voltage, V_O.

Solution

Making use of the Miller Effect, we can represent the circuit of Figure 5-3 as shown in Figure 5-5. First, let us compute the value of R_2'.

$$R_2' = \frac{R_2}{1 + A} = \frac{10 \text{ k}\Omega}{1 + 1000} \simeq 10 \, \Omega.$$

Note that the value of R_2' is quite small. This is becausd R_2 is divided by the gain of the op amp, a large number. Reference to Figure 5-5 reveals that R_2' is in parallel with the input impedance of the op amp, Z_I. Since R_2' (10 Ω) is much smaller than Z_I (50 kΩ), we can neglect the effect of the input impedance. Thus, the input circuit is composed of a simple voltage divider consisting of R_1 and R_2'. We can compute the value of V_{I_2} as follows:

$$V_{I_2} = \frac{V_S R_2'}{R_1 + R_2'} = \frac{1 \text{ V}(10 \, \Omega)}{1 \text{ k}\Omega + 10 \, \Omega} \simeq 0.01 \text{ V}.$$

Note that the value of V_{I_2} is much smaller than the value of the source voltage, V_S. This is because the value of R_2' is much smaller than that of R_1. In fact, the voltage across the input terminals of the op amp is so small that

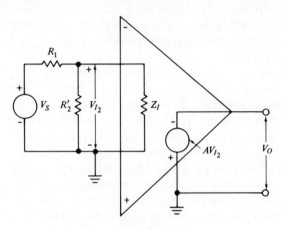

Figure 5-5

Schematic Diagram for Examples 5-1 and 5-2

we say that the terminals are effectively *shorted*. Putting it another way, we say that the minus terminal is *virtually* at ground potential. Finally, we compute the value of V_O as follows:

$$V_O = -AV_{I_2} = -(1000)(0.01 \text{ V}) = -10 \text{ V}.$$

Notice how the use of the Miller Effect simplifies the solution of the problem.

EXAMPLE 5-2

Repeat Example 5-1 assuming that the value of A has doubled to 2000.

Solution

We begin again by computing the value of R_2'.

$$R_2' = \frac{R_2}{1 + A} = \frac{10 \text{ k}\Omega}{1 + 2000} \simeq 5 \text{ }\Omega.$$

Note that *doubling* the value of A has resulted in *halving* the value of R_2'. We next compute the value of V_{I_2}.

$$V_{I_2} = \frac{V_S R_2'}{R_1 + R_2'} = \frac{(1 \text{ V})(5 \text{ }\Omega)}{1 \text{ k}\Omega + 5 \text{ }\Omega} \simeq 0.005 \text{ V}.$$

Note that V_{I_2} has also halved due to the doubling of A. Finally, we compute the value of V_O, as follows:

$$V_O = -AV_{I_2} = -(2000)(0.005 \text{ V}) = -10 \text{ V}.$$

Example 5-1 and Example 5-2 present a quantitative illustration of the negative feedback mechanism exhibited by the circuit of Figure 5-3. The doubling of the value of A (from 1000 to 2000) resulted in the halving of the value of R_2' (from 10 Ω to 5 Ω). The halving of the value of R_2' resulted in the halving of the value of V_{I_2} (from 0.01 V to 0.005 V). This halving of the value of V_{I_2} *offset* the increase in the value of A in order to keep the output voltage constant at -10 V. The results of this discussion seem to imply that we obtain perfect correction. Actually, we made some approximations in the computations. We shall see in the next section that, just as with the noninverting feedback amplifier, it is impossible to obtain perfect correction.

5-3 The Closed Loop Gain

Having discussed the feedback mechanism of the inverting amplifier, we are ready to deal with the closed loop gain. The entire inverting feedback amplifier is shown in Figure 5-6. It can be seen that the amplifier is composed

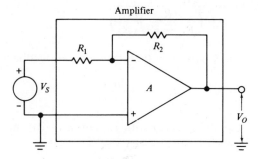

Figure 5-6

Schematic Diagram of Inverting Feedback Amplifier

of both the op amp *and* resistors R_1 and R_2. It is important to point out that R_1 is part of the amplifier, *not* the source. Recall that we assumed that the source impedance, Z_S, is equal to zero. In other words, resistor R_1 has been *intentionally* included in the amplifier. Refer now to Figure 5-5. We shall begin our derivation by obtaining an expression for V_{I_2}. We can again neglect the effect of the input impedance, Z_I, since its value is generally much larger than that of R_2'. Applying the voltage divider expression to the input circuit of Figure 5-5, we obtain the following:

$$V_{I_2} = \frac{R_2'V_S}{R_1 + R_2'} = \frac{\left(\dfrac{R_2}{1 + A}\right)V_S}{\dfrac{R_2}{1 + A} + R_1}, \tag{5-8}$$

$$V_{I_2} = \frac{R_2V_S}{R_2 + R_1(1 + A)} = \frac{R_2V_S}{R_2 + R_1 + AR_1}. \tag{5-9}$$

We may now write the expression for the output voltage as follows:

$$V_O = -AV_{I_2} = \frac{-AR_2V_S}{R_2 + R_1 + AR_1}. \tag{5-10}$$

Finally, we know that the closed loop gain, A_F, is equal to the ratio V_O/V_S. Thus, we can write the expression for A_F as follows:

$$A_F = \frac{V_O}{V_S} = \frac{-AR_2}{R_2 + R_1 + AR_1} = \frac{-\dfrac{AR_2}{R_2 + R_1}}{1 + \dfrac{AR_1}{R_2 + R_1}}, \tag{5-11}$$

$$A_F = \frac{-\dfrac{AR_2}{R_1 + R_2}}{1 + \left(\dfrac{AR_2}{R_1 + R_2}\right)\left(\dfrac{R_1}{R_2}\right)}. \tag{5-12}$$

It was mentioned in Chapter 4 that the general feedback equation is

$$A_F = \frac{A_O}{1 + A_O\beta}. \tag{4-10}$$

A comparison of Equation (5-12) with Equation (4-10) indicates that we can equate the following terms:

$$A_O = \frac{R_2A}{R_1 + R_2}, \tag{5-13}$$

$$\beta = \frac{R_1}{R_2}. \tag{5-14}$$

Equation (5-13) and Equation (5-14) apply *only* to the inverting feedback amplifier of Figure 5-6. The expression for the ideal closed loop gain may be written as follows:

$$\frac{1}{\beta} = -\frac{R_2}{R_1}. \tag{5-15}$$

The minus sign indicates polarity inversion. Equation (5-15) says that the closed loop gain is approximately equal to the ratio of the resistor values if the loop gain is much greater than one. Thus, if the loop gain is very large, we merely select values for resistors R_1 and R_2 which give us the desired value of closed loop gain. Everything said concerning gain and stability for the noninverting amplifier apply as well to the inverting amplifier

EXAMPLE 5-3

The gain of the op amp in Figure 5-6 varies from 5000 to 10,000. If $R_1 = 1$ kΩ and $R_2 = 100$ kΩ, compute the values of the closed loop gain at both temperature extremes.

Solution

First, we compute the value of β.

$$\beta = \frac{R_1}{R_2} = \frac{1 \text{ k}\Omega}{100 \text{ k}\Omega} = 0.01.$$

Next, we compute the values of A_O and A_F as follows:

(a) For $A = 5000$:

$$A_O = \frac{AR_2}{R_1 + R_2} = \frac{5000(100 \text{ k}\Omega)}{1 \text{ k}\Omega + 100 \text{ k}\Omega} \simeq 5000,$$

$$A_F = -\frac{A_O}{1 + A_O\beta} = -\frac{5000}{1 + 5000(0.01)} = -98.$$

(b) For $A = 10,000$:

$$A_O = \frac{AR_2}{R_1 + R_2} = \frac{10,000(100 \text{ k}\Omega)}{1 \text{ k}\Omega + 100 \text{ k}\Omega} \simeq 10,000,$$

$$A_F = -\frac{A_O}{1 + A_O\beta} = -\frac{10,000}{1 + 10,000(0.01)} = -99.$$

Note that while the op amp gain changes from 5000 to 10,000 (for a percentage change of 100 percent), the closed loop gain of the feedback amplifier changes from -98 to -99 (for a percentage change of 1.02 percent). The results of Example 5-3 illustrate again that improved stability is always accompanied by a reduction in the value of the gain.

As mentioned earlier, negative feedback is introduced into the inverting amplifier by the connection of resistor R_2 from the output terminal of the op amp to the minus input terminal. The path formed by this connection is known as the *feedback loop*, as shown in Figure 5-7(a). When the resistor is connected as shown in the figure, we say that the feedback loop is *closed*, and thus, the ratio of the output voltage, V_O, to the source voltage, V_S, is the

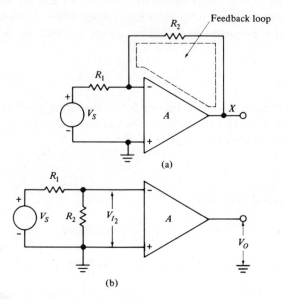

Figure 5-7

(a) The Feedback Loop; (b) The Open Loop Circuit

closed loop gain, A_F. To *open* the feedback loop, we must disconnect the terminal of R_2 which is connected to the output terminal of the op amp [terminal X in Figure 5-7(a)], and connect this terminal instead to ground. The *open* loop condition is shown in Figure 5-7(b). With resistor R_2 connected as shown in Figure 5-7(b), we say that the feedback loop is *open*, and thus, the ratio of the output voltage, V_O, to the source voltage, V_S, is the open loop gain, A_O. Using the circuit of Figure 5-7(b), we can obtain an expression for A_O as follows:

$$A_O = \frac{V_O}{V_S} = -\frac{AV_{I_2}}{V_S} = \frac{\dfrac{-AR_2V_S}{R_1 + R_2}}{V_S} = \frac{-AR_2}{R_1 + R_2}. \qquad (5\text{-}16)$$

Note the agreement between Equation (5-16) and Equation (5-13). These equations show that the open loop gain, A_O, is directly proportional to the op amp gain, A. This means that a particular variation in the value of A results in an equivalent percentage variation in the value of A_O. A_O doubles if A doubles, and so on. Thus, the feedback loop must be closed in order to improve the stability. Reference to the circuit of Figure 5-7(b) reveals that R_2 is actually in parallel with the input impedance, Z_I, of the op amp. Therefore, a more exact expression for A_O may be written as follows:

$$A_O = \frac{-A\left(\dfrac{R_2 Z_I}{R_2 + Z_I}\right)}{R_1 + \dfrac{R_2 Z_I}{R_2 + Z_I}}. \tag{5-17}$$

5-4   The Feedback Amplifier

Just as with the noninverting feedback amplifier, we should like to place the entire inverting feedback amplifier of Figure 5-6 into a black box. We begin by determining the closed loop input impedance, Z_{IF}. Figure 5-8

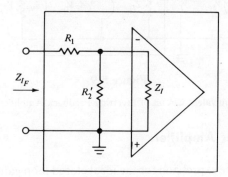

Figure 5-8

Closed Loop Input Impedance of Inverting Feedback Amplifier

shows the input circuit of the feedback amplifier. Note that this circuit is composed of three impedances. They are R_1, R_2', and Z_I. Since R_2' is in parallel with Z_I, and R_1 is in series with this parallel combination, we can write the expression for Z_{IF} as follows:

$$Z_{IF} = R_1 + \frac{R_2' Z_I}{R_2' + Z_I}. \tag{5-18}$$

We know, however, that the value of R_2' is generally much smaller than that of Z_I. Therefore, since R_2' is in parallel with Z_I, we can neglect the effect of Z_I. Similarly, we know that the value of R_2' is also much smaller than that of R_1. Therefore, since R_2' is effectively in series with R_1, we can neglect the effect of R_2'. Thus, the expression for the closed loop input impedance of the inverting feedback amplifier can be approximated as follows:

$$Z_{IF} \simeq R_1. \tag{5-19}$$

It can be shown that the expression for the closed loop output impedance of the inverting feedback amplifier is given as follows:

$$Z_{OF} = \frac{Z_O}{1 + A_O \beta}. \tag{5-20}$$

Finally, the entire feedback amplifier may be represented as shown in Figure 5-9. Note that the polarity of controlled generator $A_F V_{IF}$ indicates inversion.

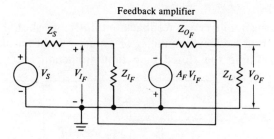

Figure 5-9

Equivalent Circuit of Inverting Feedback Amplifier

5-5   The Buffer Amplifier

We know that the expression for the ideal closed loop gain of the inverting feedback amplifier is given by $-R_2/R_1$. Thus we cannot make the value of R_1 too large without reducing the value of this gain. It was shown in the last section that the closed loop input impedance, Z_{IF}, of the inverting feedback amplifier is approximately equal to the value of resistor R_1. Thus, unlike the noninverting amplifier, which has a very large value of Z_{IF} (see Chapter 4), the inverting amplifier has a value of Z_{IF} which is not especially large. A glance at Figure 5-9 reveals that the source impedance, Z_S, and Z_{IF} comprise a voltage divider at the amplifier input. Since the value of Z_{IF} (R_1) may not always be much larger than that of Z_S, the value of V_{IF} will generally be smaller than that of V_S. If the value of V_{IF} is reduced, the values of both $A_F V_{IF}$ and V_O will also be reduced, with the result that there will be a reduction in the value of the overall gain (V_O/V_S). In other words, we say that the amplifier *loads down* the source.

More serious than the loading problem is the effect resulting from any variation in the value of Z_S. Z_S is the source impedance; that is, it depends entirely upon the source which is feeding the amplifier. It may be the internal impedance of some *transducer* (an energy-conversion device), or it may be the output impedance of some other circuit, where V_S and Z_S represent the Thevenin equivalent of that circuit. In any case, since Z_S is not necessarily a physical component (actually, it is an equivalent impedance), its value can vary with either termperature, or frequency, or both. Any variation in the value of Z_S results in serious problems, as will be illustrated by the following example:

EXAMPLE 5-4

The following data are given for an inverting feedback amplifier:

Op Amp	Feedback Network	Source	Load
$A = 5000$	$R_1 = 1 \text{ k}\Omega$	$V_S = 1 \text{ mV}$	$Z_L = \text{infinity}$
$Z_I = 100 \text{ k}\Omega$	$R_2 = 50 \text{ k}\Omega$	$Z_S = 500 \ \Omega$ to $1 \text{ k}\Omega$	
$Z_O = 100 \ \Omega$			
$Z_{Ic} = 10 \text{ M}\Omega$			

Compute the value of the output voltage, V_O, for both values of Z_S.

Solution

Refer to the general amplifier circuit shown in Figure 5-9.

(a) For $Z_S = 500 \ \Omega$:

We first apply the voltage divider expression to the input circuit to compute the value of V_{IF}.

$$V_{IF} = \frac{V_S Z_{IF}}{Z_S + Z_{IF}} = \frac{(1 \text{ mV})1 \text{ k}\Omega}{500 \ \Omega + 1 \text{ k}\Omega} = 0.67 \text{ mV}.$$

Approximating the closed loop gain by its ideal value, we get

$$A_F \simeq \frac{1}{\beta} = -\frac{R_2}{R_1} = -\frac{50 \text{ k}\Omega}{1 \text{ k}\Omega} = -50.$$

Since the output terminals of the amplifier are open-circuited ($Z_L = \text{infinity}$), we can say that the output voltage, V_O, is equal to the controlled generator voltage, $A_F V_{IF}$.

$$V_O = A_F V_{IF} = (-50)(0.67 \text{ mV}) = -33.3 \text{ mV}.$$

(b) For $Z_S = 1 \text{ k}\Omega$:

$$V_{IF} = \frac{V_S Z_{IF}}{Z_S + Z_{IF}} = \frac{(1 \text{ mV})1 \text{ k}\Omega}{1 \text{ k}\Omega + 1 \text{ k}\Omega} = 0.5 \text{ mV},$$

$$A_F = -50,$$

$$V_O = A_F V_{IF} = (-50)(0.5 \text{ mV}) = -25 \text{ mV}.$$

Note first that the value of the overall gain (V_O/V_S) is *less* than that of the closed loop gain, A_F. With $Z_S = 500\ \Omega$ the overall gain is -33.3, and with $Z_S = 1\ k\Omega$ the overall gain is -25. Both of these values are less than the closed loop gain, -50. Thus, the voltage divider at the amplifier input results in a reduction in the value of the overall gain. Second, and even more serious, is the fact that the overall gain *varies* considerably. With $V_S = 1\ mV$, the value of V_O varies from $-33.3\ mV$ to $-25\ mV$, depending upon the value of Z_S. This is highly undesirable. Recall that the purpose of introducing negative feedback is to stabilize the gain. Now, even after we have incorporated feedback, we find that the gain still varies. What is the reason for this phenomenon? Do not blame the feedback mechanism. It is doing its job, which is to stabilize the ratio of output voltage, V_O, to *amplifier* input voltage, V_{IF} (the ratio is equal to -50 in this case). The problem is caused by the loading of the source by the amplifier input circuit. Since the value of Z_{IF} ($1\ k\Omega$) is not much larger than that of Z_S($500\ \Omega$ and $1\ k\Omega$), any variation in Z_S will result in a corresponding variation in V_{IF}. This variation in V_{IF} is transmitted through the amplifier to the output circuit.

As things stand, the amplifier is quite useless. Now, what shall we do about this serious problem? The problem is caused by the fact that the value of Z_{IF} is not much larger than that of Z_S. In other words, the source would like to "see" a very *large input impedance*. Putting it another way, the amplifier would like to be fed from a source having a very *small output impedance*. Do we know of a circuit that has a very large input impedance and a very small output impedance? You should see that this is an ideal application for the voltage follower. The follower is connected between the source and the amplifier as shown in Figure 5-10. The following example will illustrate the improvement in circuit performance resulting from the use of the follower:

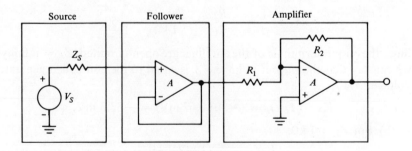

Figure 5-10

The Follower Used as a Buffer Amplifier

EXAMPLE 5-5

Repeat Example 5-4, except connect the follower between the source and the amplifier as shown in Figure 5-10. Assume that the same type op amp used in the amplifier is also used in the follower.

Solution

We begin by representing both the source and the follower by their equivalent circuits as shown in Figure 5-11. Next, we compute the values of A_F, Z_{IF}, and Z_{OF} for the follower:

$$A_F \simeq 1,$$

$$Z_{IF} = \frac{(A_0 Z_I) Z_{Ic}}{A_0 Z_I + Z_{Ic}} = \frac{(5000)(100 \text{ k}\Omega)(10 \text{ M}\Omega)}{(5000)(100 \text{ k}\Omega) + 10 \text{ M}\Omega} \simeq 10 \text{ M}\Omega,$$

$$Z_{OF} = \frac{Z_0}{A_0} = \frac{100 \text{ }\Omega}{5000} = 0.02 \text{ }\Omega.$$

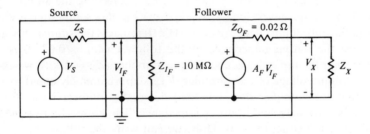

Figure 5-11

Schematic Diagram for Example 5-5

Notice in Figure 5-11 that since the source is connected to the input of the follower instead of the amplifier, it sees the very *large* input impedance of the follower (10 MΩ) instead of the relatively *small* input impedance of the amplifier (1 kΩ). Since the 10 MΩ input impedance of the follower is much larger than *either the 500 Ω or the 1 kΩ* value of source impedance, we can say that the input voltage to the follower, V_{IF}, is approximately equal to the source voltage, 1 mV. In other words, the variation in the value of Z_S has practically no effect on the value of V_{IF}. We say that the large input impedance of the follower *swamps out* the variation in the value of Z_S. Since the voltage gain of the follower is equal to unity, the value of the controlled voltage generator, $A_F V_{IF}$, in Figure 5-11 is equal to 1 mV. Note that the output circuit of the follower is fed to an impedance called Z_X. To avoid confusion, we have used Z_X to represent the input impedance of the amplifier.

The equivalent circuits of the output of the follower and the amplifier are shown in Figure 5-12. Note that we can consider the output circuit

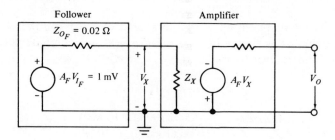

Figure 5-12

Schematic Diagram for Example 5-5

of the follower as representing a *source* which is feeding the amplifier. The controlled voltage generator ($A_F V_{IF} = 1$ mV) replaces the source voltage, V_S, and the output impedance ($Z_{OF} = 0.02 \, \Omega$) replaces the source impedance, Z_S. Since the output impedance of the follower ($Z_{OF} = 0.02 \, \Omega$) is much smaller than the input impedance of the amplifier ($Z_X = 1 \, k\Omega$), we can say that the input voltage of the amplifier, V_X, is approximately equal to 1 mV. Note that the amplifier does *not* load down the follower because of the follower's extremely small output impedance. The closed loop gain of the amplifier is still equal to -50. Thus, we can write the following:

$$V_O = A_F V_X = (-50)(1 \text{ mV}) = -50 \text{ mV}.$$

Now let us discuss the benefits achieved from using the follower. First, we see that the overall gain of the amplifier (follower + feedback amplifier) is equal to -50. There has been no loss in voltage due to loading because the follower presents a large impedance to the source. More important, the output voltage remains constant at -50 mV regardless of the value of the source impedance, Z_S. Herein lies the beauty of the follower circuit. It presents a large impedance to the source. This effect swamps out any variation in the value of the source impedance by making the input voltage to the follower, V_{IF}, approximately constant and equal to the source voltage, V_S (1 mV). Since the gain of the follower is equal to unity, the value of the controlled voltage generator, $A_F V_{IF}$, is *also* equal to the source voltage (1 mV). Finally, since the output impedance of the follower is very small, we can say that the output voltage of the follower, V_X (which is also the input voltage of the amplifier) is approximately equal to the value of the controlled voltage generator, which in turn is equal to the source voltage (1 mV). In other words, due to its large input impedance, unity gain, and small output impedance, the follower *transfers* the source voltage, virtually undisturbed, from the source to the amplifier input terminals.

The results of the preceding discussion imply that the follower is used to *separate* the amplifier from the source; that is, it is used to prevent the amplifier from loading down the source. It is for this reason that we call the follower a *buffer*. A buffer is something that separates, or minimizes the effects of two things upon each other. Although the follower is not an amplifier in the usual sense, it is sometimes referred to as a buffer amplifier.

5-6   The Differential Amplifier

In the past few chapters, we have discussed methods of introducing feedback into amplifiers having a single input. Since one of the major assets of the op amp is its ability to amplify the algebraic difference between two voltages, we should like to be able to use it as a differential amplifier and at the same time maintain a constant gain. We could connect two feedback resistors, R_A and R_B, to the op amp as shown in Figure 5-13.

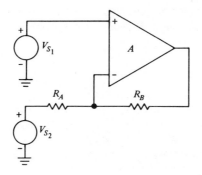

Figure 5-13

Differential Amplifier with Unequal Gains

Note that two source voltages, V_{S_1} and V_{S_2}, are applied to the plus and minus terminals of the op amp, respectively. We shall assume that both source impedances are equal to zero.

Let us derive an expression for the output voltage, V_O, to determine whether or not the circuit of Figure 5-13 is functioning as a differential feedback amplifier. To accomplish this, we shall make use of the Superposition theorem. This theorem states that we can determine the value of the output voltage by finding the response due to each source *separately*, and then combining the results. To begin, we *short* source V_{S_2}, as shown in Figure 5-14(a). Observation of the circuit reveals that what remains is a

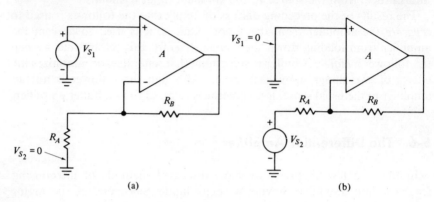

(a)   (b)

Figure 5-14

Superposition Theorem Applied to Circuit of Figure 5-13

simple noninverting feedback amplifier using feedback resistors R_A and R_B. Using the expression for the ideal closed loop gain, we can express the output voltage *due to source V_{S_1} only* as follows:

$$V_O = A_F V_{S_1},$$

$$V_O = \left(\frac{R_B + R_A}{R_A}\right)V_{S_1}. \tag{5-21}$$

Similarly, we can short source V_{S_1}, as shown in Figure 5-14(b). Note that the remaining circuit is simply an inverting feedback amplifier which also uses feedback resistors R_A and R_B. Again using the expression for the ideal closed loop gain, we can express the output voltage *due to source V_{S_2} only* as follows:

$$V_O = A_F V_{S_2},$$

$$V_O = -\left(\frac{R_B}{R_A}\right)V_{S_2}. \tag{5-22}$$

Now, we may combine these two expressions to obtain the *total* output voltage:

$$V_O = \left(\frac{R_B + R_A}{R_A}\right)V_{S_1} - \left(\frac{R_B}{R_A}\right)V_{S_2}. \tag{5-23}$$

We can see now that the output voltage may be expressed as the *difference* between two terms, one proportional to the value of source voltage V_{S_1}, and the other to that of source voltage V_{S_2}. However, a more careful examination of Equation (5-23) reveals that something is wrong. The gain of the amplifier for source V_{S_1} $(1 + R_B/R_A)$ is *larger* than the gain for source V_{S_2} $(-R_B/R_A)$. This results from the fact that the gains of the noninverting and inverting amplifiers are not equal. If the gains are not equal, the output voltage will *not* be directly proportional to the algebraic difference between voltages V_{S_1} and V_{S_2}. Thus, we should like the gains for both source voltage V_{S_1} and V_{S_2} to be equal. Since both gains depend upon the values of resistors R_A and R_B, we cannot change the value of either of these resistors without changing the values of both gains. Thus, we shall have to insert additional circuitry into the amplifier of Figure 5-13.

It is easier to reduce the gain of the noninverting amplifier than to increase the gain of the inverting amplifier. We shall multiply the non-inverting gain by some factor, X, and set this product equal to the inverting gain, as follows:

$$\left(\frac{R_B + R_A}{R_A}\right) X = \frac{R_B}{R_A}. \tag{5-24}$$

Solving Equation (5-24) for X, we get

$$X = \left(\frac{R_B}{R_A}\right)\left(\frac{R_A}{R_A + R_B}\right) = \frac{R_B}{R_A + R_B}. \tag{5-25}$$

Equation (5-25) says that we must reduce the noninverting gain by the factor $R_B/(R_B + R_A)$ in order that it be equal to the inverting gain. This can be accomplished by inserting a voltage divider between source V_{S_1} and the plus terminal of the op amp, as shown in Figure 5-15. We can still

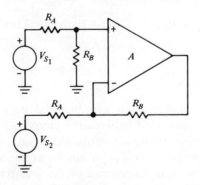

Figure 5-15

Differential Amplifier with Equal Gains

express the output voltage due to source V_{S_2} only by Equation (5-22). Now, due to the presence of the voltage divider, we can express the output voltage due to source V_{S_1} only as follows:

$$V_O = \left(\frac{R_B}{\cancel{R_A + R_B}}\right)\left(\frac{\cancel{R_A + R_B}}{R_A}\right)V_{S_1} = \left(\frac{R_B}{R_A}\right)V_{S_1}. \qquad (5\text{-}26)$$

Thus, the gains for both source voltage V_{S_1} and V_{S_2} are now equal, and the total output voltage can be expressed as follows:

$$V_O = \left(\frac{R_B}{R_A}\right)V_{S_1} - \left(\frac{R_B}{R_A}\right)V_{S_2},$$

$$V_O = \frac{R_B}{R_A}(V_{S_1} - V_{S_2}). \qquad (5\text{-}27)$$

Equation (5-27) says that the output voltage is directly proportional to the algebraic difference between source voltages V_{S_1} and V_{S_2}. The circuit of Figure 5-15 is a differential feedback amplifier whose gain is equal to R_B/R_A.

EXAMPLE 5-6

The following data are given for the circuit of Figure 5-15:

$$R_A = 1 \text{ k}\Omega \qquad V_{S_1} = +10 \text{ mV dc}$$
$$R_B = 20 \text{ k}\Omega \qquad V_{S_2} = +2 \text{ mV dc}$$

Compute the value of the output voltage, V_O.

Solution

Substituting into Equation (5-27), we get:

$$V_O = \frac{R_B}{R_A}(V_{S_1} - V_{S_2}) = \frac{20 \text{ k}\Omega}{1 \text{ k}\Omega}(+10 \text{ mV} - 2 \text{ mV}) = +160 \text{ mV}.$$

SUMMARY

1.   The inverting configuration can be used as a feedback amplifier.
2.   An impedance connected between the input and output terminals can be considered as being connected across the input terminals if its value is divided by the factor $(1 + A)$. This is known as the Miller Effect.
3.   The closed loop input impedance of the inverting feedback amplifier is relatively small. This results in the amplifier's loading down the source.
4.   The voltage follower is used as a buffer to prevent the amplifier from loading down the source.

5. By employing the proper connection of resistors, it is possible to use the op amp as a differential feedback amplifier.

PROBLEMS

5-1. The following data are given for an inverting feedback amplifier:

Op Amp	Feedback Network
$A = 50{,}000$ to $100{,}000$	$R_1 = 1\ k\Omega$
$Z_I = 20\ k\Omega$	$R_2 = 500\ k\Omega$
$Z_O = 50\ \Omega$	
$Z_{IC} = 20\ M\Omega$	

(a) Compute the value of the closed loop gain at both temperature extremes.

(b) Compute the percentage change in the closed loop gain.

(c) Compute the value of the loop gain at both temperature extremes.

(d) Compute the value of the ideal closed loop gain.

5-2. Repeat Problem 5-1, except make $R_2 = 100\ k\Omega$. Compare the results with those of Problem 5-1 and explain.

5-3. Repeat Problem 5-1, except make $R_2 = 50\ k\Omega$. Compare the results with those of Problem 5-2 and explain.

5-4. The amplifier of Problem 5-3 is fed from a source whose V_S is a 1 mV peak sine wave and whose Z_S is zero ohms. Sketch the waveform of the output voltage, V_O.

5-5. What is the phase angle between V_S and V_O in Problem 5-4? Explain.

5-6. Compute the value of the closed loop input impedance in Problem 5-4.

5-7. Compute the value of the closed loop output impedance in Problem 5-4.

5-8. The amplifier of Problem 5-3 is fed from a source whose V_S is $+1$ mV dc and whose Z_S varies from 1 kΩ to 5 kΩ. Compute the value of V_O for both values of Z_S.

5-9. Repeat Problem 5-8, except place a follower between the source and the amplifier. Use the same type op amp for the follower as was used in Problem 5-1.

5-10. A differential amplifier has $R_A = 1\ k\Omega$ and $R_B = 20\ k\Omega$. Compute the value of V_O if $V_{S_1} = +40$ mV dc and $V_{S_2} = -1$ mV dc.

5-11. Repeat Problem 5-10 if $V_{S_1} = -20$ mV dc and $V_{S_2} = +20$ mV dc.

6

dc Offset
and Drift

At this point, you may feel that you are quite knowledgeable on the subject of op amps. You know that the op amp may be used as a non-inverting, inverting, or differential amplifier, and that negative feedback can be introduced to stabilize the gain. However, do not become complacent. There are quite a few aspects of the op amp that you have not yet studied.

Up to this point we have not distinguished between dc and ac input signals. We have treated the op amp as though it responded equally to both types of voltages. Although the op amp can amplify both dc and ac signals, the design of the associated circuitry depends to some extent upon the nature of the input. In particular, the design of a dc amplifier is considerably more difficult than one might expect at first glance. The practical op amp has certain properties that limit the accuracy of any dc amplifier of which it is a part. In this chapter we shall discuss these properties in some detail, indicating the manner in which they limit the accuracy of the amplifier. We shall see that it is necessary to incorporate additional circuitry to increase the effectiveness of the amplifier. In other words, we have a whole new set of problems to deal with.

114

6-1   The Offset Voltage

Recall from Chapter 3 that that the behavior of an op amp can be represented graphically by a curve known as the voltage transfer characteristic, as shown in Figure 6-1. This is a graph of output voltage, V_O,

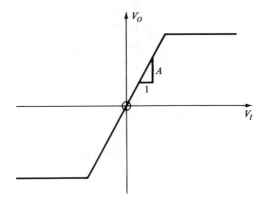

Figure 6-1

Ideal Voltage Transfer Characteristic

plotted against input difference voltage, V_I. We also showed in Chapter 3 that since the curve is a straight line (excluding saturation), we can write the following equations:

$$V_O = AV_I + 0, \qquad\qquad (3\text{-}2)$$

$$y = mx + b. \qquad\qquad (3\text{-}3)$$

Equating terms, we get

$$b = V_O\text{-intercept} = \text{zero}, \qquad\qquad (3\text{-}4)$$

$$m = \text{slope} = A \text{ (gain of the op amp).} \qquad\qquad (3\text{-}5)$$

Equation (3-4) tells us that the V_O-intercept, b, is equal to zero. What does this mean? It means simply that the voltage transfer characteristic passes through the origin. This can also be ascertained from an inspection of Figure 6-1. The fact that the curve passes through the origin has important significance. It says that when the input difference voltage, V_I, is equal to zero, the output voltage, V_O, is *also* equal to zero. It is extremely important that op amps which are to be used in dc amplifiers have voltage transfer characteristics such as the one shown in Figure 6-1. The curve in Figure 6-1 is actually an *ideal* voltage transfer characteristic. The term "ideal" is used because it is impossible to obtain such a curve in practice.

Because of manufacturing limitations, the voltage transfer characteristics of practical op amps will *not* pass through the origin. The curve exhibited by a practical op amp will generally appear as shown in Figure 6-2. Before

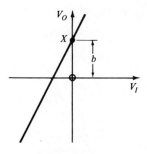

Figure 6-2

Practical Voltage Transfer Characteristic

proceeding, it should be mentioned that the curve of Figure 6-2 is *not* drawn to scale. The dimensions have been deliberately exaggerated in order to illustrate some significant concepts. If drawn to scale the curve would be much steeper and closer to the origin. Notice in Figure 6-2 that the curve intersects the V_O-axis at point X, not at the origin. In other words, there is a *finite* (nonzero) V_O-intercept, b. Thus, we may write the equation of the curve as follows:

$$V_O = AV_I + b. \tag{6-1}$$

Let us see what happens when the value of the input difference voltage, V_I, is equal to zero. Substituting into Equation (6-1) we get

$$V_O = A(0) + b = b. \tag{6-2}$$

Now, here is an important point. Equation (6-2) tells us that when the input voltage is equal to zero ($V_I = 0$), the output voltage is *not* equal to zero ($V_O = b$). In other words, we have a finite output even though the input is equal to zero. A dc amplifier is not supposed to work this way. In a dc amplifier, we always want the output voltage to be *directly proportional* to the input voltage. This implies, of course, that we should like the output voltage to be zero when the input voltage is zero. This is obviously *not* the case with the op amp whose voltage transfer characteristic is shown in Figure 6-2. The condition illustrated in Figure 6-2 is responsible for a serious limitation in the accuracy of a dc amplifier. We shall have more to say about this point later.

We now define a new term known as the *offset voltage referred to the input*, V_{OS}:

V_{OS} = the offset voltage referred to the input.

V_{OS} is the value of input difference voltage, V_I, at which the output voltage, V_O, is equal to zero. We can determine this value quite simply by making use of Equation (6-1). We merely substitute $V_O = 0$ and solve for V_I as follows:

$$V_O = 0 = AV_I + b, \tag{6-3}$$

$$V_I = \frac{-b}{A}, \tag{6-4}$$

$$V_{OS} = \frac{-b}{A}. \tag{6-5}$$

Equation (6-5) says that V_{OS} is equal to minus the value of the V_O-intercept, b, divided by the gain of the op amp, A.

The graphical significance of V_{OS} is illustrated in Figure 6-3. Figure 6-3(a) shows the voltage transfer characteristic of a practical op amp

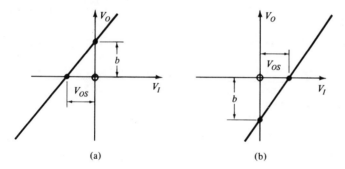

(a)   (b)

Figure 6-3

(a) Transfer Characteristic with Negative V_{OS}; (b) Transfer Characteristic with Positive V_{OS}

Note that V_{OS} is the value of input voltage at which the output voltage is equal to zero. We can see now why the term "offset" was used. A glance at Figure 6-3(a) reveals that the voltage transfer characteristic is *set off* from the origin. The V_O-intercept, b, is a measure of the *vertical* offset and V_{OS} is a measure of the *horizontal* offset. Equation (6-5) says that the polarity of V_{OS} is always opposite to that of b. Thus, when b is positive as in Figure 6-3(a), V_{OS} is negative. Due to statistical variations in production yield, it is possible for b to be negative, as in Figure 6-3(b). In this case, V_{OS} is positive.

Since the manufacturer generally specifies the value of V_{OS}, and not b, it is advisable to rewrite Equation (6-1) as follows:

$$V_O = AV_I + b.$$

Since

$$V_{OS} = \frac{-b}{A},$$

then

$$b = -AV_{OS}.$$

Thus,

$$V_O = AV_I - AV_{OS},$$

$$V_O = A(V_I - V_{OS}). \tag{6-6}$$

Values of V_{OS} for practical op amps are usually plus or minus a few millivolts. Although this value sounds small, it can have a very detrimental effect upon the performance of a dc amplifier.

EXAMPLE 6-1

An op amp has a gain of 5000 and an offset voltage of $+1$ mV. Find the value of the output voltage when the input voltage is equal to zero.

Solution

To solve this problem we merely substitute into Equation (6-6), setting $V_I = 0$.

$$V_O = A(V_I - V_{OS}) = A(0 - V_{OS}) = -AV_{OS},$$

$$V_O = -(5000)(+1 \text{ mV}) = -5 \text{ V}.$$

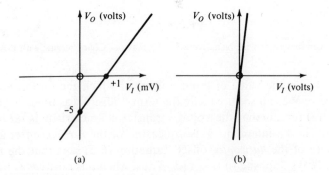

(a)   (b)

Figure 6-4

(a) Transfer Characteristic for Example 6-1; (b) Transfer Characteristic Drawn to Scale

When the input difference voltage to the op amp of Example 6-1 is zero, the output voltage is -5 V. This is quite a large error. The voltage transfer characteristic is shown in Figure 6-4(a). Notice in Figure 6-4(a) that the vertical (V_O) axis has units of volts, while the horizontal (V_I) axis has units of millivolts. This accounts for the relatively gradual slope of the characteristic in Figure 6-4(a). If both axes had the same units, say volts, the characteristic would appear as shown in Figure 6-4(b).

6-2   Offset Voltage Compensation

We saw in the last section that the existence of the offset voltage presents a serious problem. The next logical step is to determine a method which can be used to either eliminate or minimize the *effect* of offset. Notice that we used the term "effect." We cannot eliminate the offset voltage itself because all op amps have some offset resulting from limitations imposed by mass-production techniques. Therefore, since we cannot eliminate the offset voltage, we shall have to find some means of *compensating* for it.

Let us see how this is done. An inverting amplifier is shown in Figure 6-5.

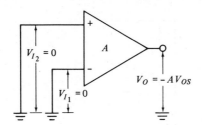

Figure 6-5

Uncompensated Op Amp

Notice that since the plus terminal is always grounded in an inverting amplifier, $V_{I_1} = 0$. Recall that the actual input voltage to an inverting amplifier is V_{I_2}, the voltage between the minus terminal and ground. When the minus terminal is grounded, as shown in Figure 6-5, $V_{I_2} = 0$. Let us find the value of V_O when $V_{I_2} = 0$. To accomplish this, we substitute into Equation (6-6), setting both V_{I_1} and V_{I_2} equal to zero.

$$V_O = A(V_I - V_{OS}) = A(V_{I_1} - V_{I_2} - V_{OS}), \qquad (6\text{-}7)$$

$$V_O = A(0 - V_{OS}) = -AV_{OS}. \qquad (6\text{-}8)$$

Thus, we see again that although the input voltage is equal to zero ($V_{I_2} = 0$), the output voltage is *not* equal to zero ($V_O = -AV_{OS}$).

We can compensate for the error introduced by the offset voltage. Instead of grounding the positive terminal of the op amp as we always do, we insert a voltage between this terminal and ground. In other words, we set V_{I_1} equal to some value which *cancels* the effect of the offset voltage. What value of V_{I_1} cancels the effect of the offset voltage? First, let us rewrite Equation (6-7).

$$V_O = A(V_{I_1} - V_{I_2} - V_{OS}).$$ (6-7)

Since V_{I_2} is the actual input voltage to the inverting amplifier, we should like V_O to be equal to zero when V_{I_2} is equal to zero. Thus, we substitute into Equation (6-7), setting V_{I_2} and V_O equal to zero, and solve for V_{I_1}.

$$0 = A(V_{I_1} - 0 - V_{OS}),$$ (6-9)

$$V_{I_1} = V_{OS}.$$ (6-10)

Equation (6-10) says that we must insert a voltage between the plus terminal and ground equal to the offset voltage, V_{OS}, as shown in Figure 6-6. The circuit of Figure 6-6 is compensated for offset voltage. To prove that this

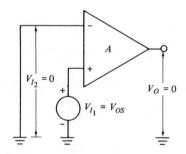

Figure 6-6

Compensated Op Amp

is so we merely substitute into Equation (6-7), setting $V_{I_2} = 0$ and $V_{I_1} = V_{OS}$.

$$V_O = A(V_{OS} - 0 - V_{OS}) = 0.$$ (6-11)

Equation (6-11) indicates that when offset compensation is introduced, V_O is equal to zero when V_{I_2} is equal to zero.

Just as with the gain of the op amp, the offset voltage varies somewhat from unit to unit because of mass-production techniques. We have also seen that the offset voltage may be either positive or negative. For these reasons we should like to have some method of adjusting the compensating voltage to allow for variations in the value of V_{OS}. This can be done by making use of the potentiometer arrangement shown in Figure 6-7. Potentiometer R_X is connected between the positive and negative dc power

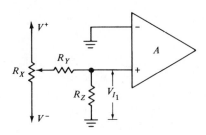

Figure   6-7

Compensating Circuit

supplies. The wiper of the potentiometer is connected to the plus terminal of the op amp through a resistive divider composed of R_Y and R_Z. By moving the wiper, we can adjust the value of V_{I_1} to compensate for varying values of offset voltage.

Now, let us study the compensating circuit in some detail. We begin by examining the portion of the circuit to the left of R_Y in Figure 6-7. This portion of the circuit is composed of the two dc power supplies (V^+ and V^-) and potentiometer R_X, as shown in Figure 6-8(a). We shall replace

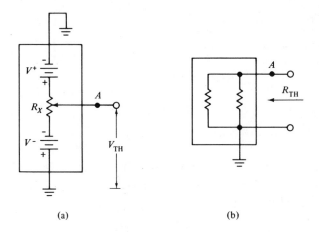

(a)   (b)

Figure   6-8

Analysis of Compensating Circuit

this circuit by its Thevenin equivalent. The value of the open circuit Thevenin voltage, V_{TH} (the potential at point A with respect to ground), depends upon the position of the potentiometer wiper, as follows:

When the wiper is at the upper end of R_X: $V_{TH} = V^+$ (positive voltage).
When the wiper is at the lower end of R_X: $V_{TH} = V^-$ (negative voltage).
When the wiper at the center of R_X: $V_{TH} = 0$.

To find the Thevenin resistance, R_{TH}, we short both power supplies and look into the circuit between point A and ground, as shown in Figure 6-8(b). R_{TH} is equal to the parallel equivalent of two resistances. These are the values of resistance between the wiper and either end of potentiometer R_X. Just as with V_{TH}, the value of R_{TH} depends upon the position of the wiper. It can be shown that R_{TH} has its maximum value when the wiper is positioned at the center of R_X. In this case, the values of the resistances in Figure 6-8(b) are each equal to one-half the value of the potentiometer resistance, or $R_X/2$. Thus, the maximum value of R_{TH} is equal to the parallel equivalent of these two resistances, or $R_X/4$.

We may now represent the compensating circuit as shown in Figure 6-9(a). The value of R_{TH} is usually much smaller than that of R_Y. Thus, the circuit

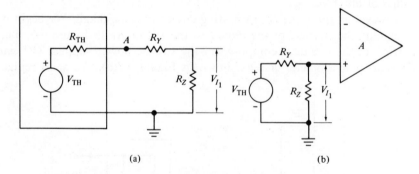

(a)   (b)

Figure 6-9

Analysis of Compensating Circuit

of Figure 6-9(a) may be redrawn as shown in Figure 6-9(b). Applying the voltage divider expression to the circuit of Figure 6-9(b), we can write the following equation:

$$V_{I_1} = \frac{(V_{TH})R_Z}{R_Y + R_Z}. \tag{6-12}$$

We have seen that the value of V_{TH} can be as large as the values of the dc power supply voltages, V^+ and V^-. However, we want the value of V_{I_1}

to be only as large as the maximum expected offset voltage specified by the manufacturer. Therefore, since the maximum value of V_{I_1} will be much smaller than the maximum value of V_{TH}, we use the voltage divider composed of R_Y and R_Z to scale down the voltage. As a result of the large difference in the magnitudes of V_I and V_{TH}, the value of R_Y will be much larger than that of R_Z. Thus, Equation (6-12) may be approximated as follows:

$$V_{I_1} \simeq \frac{(V_{TH})R_Z}{R_Y}.$$ (6-13)

We know that the value of V_{TH} can be made as large as the values of V^+ and V^-. Assuming that the values of V^+ and V^- are equal ($V^+ = V^- = V$), we can say that the maximum value of V_{TH} is equal to V. Similarly, we want to be able to make the value of V_{I_1} as large as the maximum expected offset voltage. Thus, we say that the maximum value of V_{I_1} is equal to V_{OS}. Substituting these values into Equation (6-13), we get

$$V_{OS} = \frac{(V)R_Z}{R_Y},$$ (6-14)

$$\frac{V_{OS}}{V} = \frac{R_Z}{R_Y}.$$ (6-15)

Thus, the values of both the power supply voltages and the maximum expected offset voltage determine the required voltage divider ratio.

EXAMPLE 6-2

The manufacturer of a particular op amp specifies that the maximum offset voltage is plus or minus 2 mV. The op amp uses 10 V power supplies. Design the compensating circuit.

Solution

We know that the required voltage divider ratio is given by Equation (6-15). Substituting into the equation, we get

$$\frac{R_Z}{R_Y} = \frac{V_{OS}}{V} = \frac{2 \text{ mV}}{10 \text{ V}} = \frac{1}{5000}.$$

This gives the required ratio of R_Z/R_Y. If we select $R_Z = 10 \ \Omega$, the value of R_Y should be:

$$R_Y = 5000(R_Z) = 5000(10 \ \Omega) = 50 \text{ k}\Omega.$$

It was mentioned previously that the value of R_Y is generally much larger than that of R_{TH}. Thus, if we make the value of R_Y much larger than the *maximum* value of R_{TH} ($R_X/4$), our approximations will retain their validity. Therefore, we shall make $R_X/4$ equal to 5 kΩ. which means that R_X must be a 20 kΩ potentiometer. The final circuit is shown in Figure 6-10.

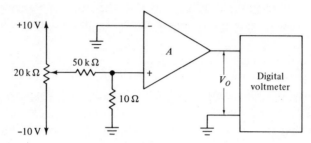

Figure 6-10

Nulling Procedure

The procedure for compensating or "nulling" the op amp is as follows:

1. Ground the minus terminal of the op amp. This sets $V_{I_2} = 0$.
2. Connect a digital voltmeter across the output terminals.
3. Vary the position of the potentiometer wiper until the voltmeter reads zero. The op amp is now compensated.
4. Remove the minus terminal from ground and connect it to the source.

6-3   Drift

In the last section we learned that all practical op amps have some finite value of offset voltage. We saw, however, that we can compensate for this effect in the inverting amplifier by injecting a voltage into the noninverting (plus) input. If the situation were no more complicated than this, we could end the chapter right here. However, things are not as simple as they seem. There are a few important concepts that we have not yet discussed. Chief among these concepts is the fact that the value of the offset voltage *varies*. It varies with three quantities:

1. Temperature
2. Power supply voltages (V^+ and V^-)
3. Time

The quantity that causes the most serious variation in the value of offset voltage is temperature. The rate of change of offset voltage with temperature is called *thermal drift*. Since we shall be dealing primarily with the effects of temperature, we shall refer to the variation simply as drift.

$$\frac{\Delta V_{OS}}{\Delta T} = \textbf{drift.}$$

The value of drift is usually specified in microvolts per degree Centigrade, $\mu V/°C$. It is important to mention that the *drift itself* is not a constant value. This means that the value of the offset voltage may vary more in one temperature range than in another. For example, the drift may be equal to 5 $\mu V/°C$ between 20°C and 30°C, and equal to 20 $\mu V/°C$ between 80°C and 90°C. Even more important, it is possible for the offset voltage to *in*crease with increasing temperature, and then at some point begin to *de*crease even though the temperature is still increasing. In other words, the drift may be *positive* in one temperature range, and *negative* in another.

In view of this large variation in the value of the drift, how does the manufacturer specify information concerning its behavior? Some manufacturers provide the user with a graph of offset voltage versus temperature. Others specify the *average* value of drift over a large temperature range. Still others indicate the *maximum* value of drift for a particular op amp. In this text, we shall follow the last of these three approaches.

EXAMPLE 6-3

A particular op amp has a value of offset voltage equal to 2 mV at room temperature (25°C). The manufacturer specifies that the maximum value of drift for this type of op amp is 10 $\mu V/°C$. Compute the value of the offset voltage at 95°C.

Solution

Since the drift is the rate of change of offset voltage with temperature, we can compute the *change* in offset voltage by multiplying the drift by the change in temperature.

$$\Delta V_{OS} = \left(\frac{\Delta V_{OS}}{\Delta T}\right)(\Delta T).$$

The change in temperature is 70°C (95 minus 25). Thus, the change in offset voltage is

$$\Delta V_{OS} = (10 \ \mu V/°C)(70°C) = 700 \ \mu V = 0.7 \ mV.$$

Since the maximum drift may be either positive or negative, the *new* value of V_{OS} (at 95° C) may be either larger or smaller than the *old* value (at 25°C).

$$V_{OS}(95°C) = V_{OS}(25°C) + \Delta V_{OS},$$

$$V_{OS}(95°C) = 2\text{ mV} + 0.7\text{ mV} = 2.7\text{ mV},$$

or

$$V_{OS}(95°C) = 2\text{ mV} - 0.7\text{ mV} = 1.3\text{ mV}.$$

Note that as a result of drift, the value of V_{OS} has changed significantly.

Now, here is an important point. The equations seem to predict that the offset voltage will change (or drift) an amount equal to 0.7 mV. In our computations, we used the maximum value of drift. This means that the *maximum* change in offset voltage is 0.7 mV. Is it possible that the change in offset voltage between 25°C and 95°C is *less* than 0.7 mV? The answer is yes. We shall see later in the chapter that the effectiveness of a dc amplifier is inversely proportional to the value of the op amp drift. In other words, the larger the drift, the poorer the amplifier. It is for this reason that we investigate the performance of a dc amplifier at the condition of maximum drift. This is known as *worst case* design. If the amplifier performs adequately under the worst conditions (maximum drift), its performance will obviously be acceptable under more favorable circumstances.

EXAMPLE 6-4

Compute the change in offset voltage in Example 6-3 if the maximum value of drift is 1 μV/°C.

Solution

$$\Delta V_{OS} = (1\ \mu\text{V}/°\text{C})(70°\text{C}) = 70\ \mu\text{V} = 0.07\text{ mV}.$$

Comparing the results of Example 6-4 with those of Example 6-3, we see that a small value of drift results in a small change in offset voltage.

Drift, not offset, is the major problem in the design of dc amplifiers. The *initial* offset (the offset at room temperature) can always be cancelled by use of the potentiometer arrangement discussed in the last section. However, this procedure compensates for offset *only at room temperature*. Once the temperature changes, the offset voltage will drift (change). This would seem to necessitate a readjustment of the offset voltage each time the temperature changes. This is impractical for two reasons: First, it is troublesome to keep readjusting the op amp. Second, the amplifier is often located in areas where readjustment is impossible, such as in missiles or space capsules. Thus, we have to "live with" drift. We shall have more to say about drift later.

6-4   The Offset Current

In addition to offset voltage, there is another factor which is detrimental to the performance of a dc amplifier. In order to simplify the study of this factor, we shall assume that the offset voltage is equal to zero for the duration of this section. Figure 6-11 shows an op amp with both input

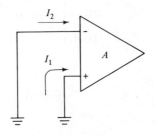

Figure 6-11

Bias Currents

terminals grounded. This means that there is no input voltage to the op amp. Recall from Chapter 1, however, that it is necessary to supply dc power to the amplifier in order to bias it properly. Therefore, even though the input voltage to the op amp is zero, two dc bias currents, I_1 and I_2, flow into the transistors in the two input stages of the op amp, as shown in Figure 6-11.

I_1 = the dc bias current flowing into the plus input

I_2 = the dc bias current flowing into the minus input.

Figure 6-12(a) shows a typical inverting amplifier. We have omitted resistor R_2 temporarily in order to simplify the following discussion. Note that source voltage V_{S_2} is the actual input voltage to the amplifier. For proper dc amplifier operation, we want the output voltage, V_O, to be equal to zero when the input voltage, V_{S_2}, is equal to zero. Let us see if this is so.

Figure 6-12(b) shows the amplifier with source voltage V_{S_2} set equal to zero. Note that bias current I_2 flows through resistor R_1, resulting in a voltage drop across R_1 having the polarity shown. A glance at Figure 6-12(b) reveals that the value of V_{I_2} is *finite* due to the voltage drop across R_1. Applying Ohm's law, we can express the value of V_{I_2} as follows:

$$V_{I_2} = -I_2R_1. \tag{6-16}$$

The value of V_{I_1} is equal to zero because the plus terminal of the op amp is grounded.

$$V_{I_1} = 0. \tag{6-17}$$

We may now substitute into Equation (6-7) to determine the value of the output voltage. Remember that we assumed that the offset voltage, V_{OS}, is equal to zero.

$$V_O = A(V_{I_1} - V_{I_2}), \tag{6-7}$$

$$V_O = A(0 - (-I_2 R_1)), \tag{6-18}$$

$$V_O = A(I_2 R_1). \tag{6-19}$$

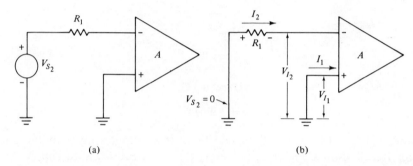

(a)   (b)

Figure 6-12

Approximate Circuit for Computing Offset Due to Bias Currents

Note that Equation (6-19) says that the output voltage, V_O, is *not* equal to zero even though the source voltage, V_{S_2}, is equal to zero. But how can this be? We have already assumed that the offset voltage is zero. The answer is that V_{OS} has nothing whatsoever to do with this situation. The finite value of output voltage is due to the voltage drop across resistor R_1, which in turn is caused by bias current I_2. In other words, the voltage drop resulting from the bias current has the *effect* of producing an offset voltage. The equivalent offset voltage for the circuit of Figure 6-12 is equal to the voltage drop across resistor R_1, namely $I_2 R_1$.

EXAMPLE 6-5

Compute the value of the equivalent offset voltage in the circuit of Figure 6-12 if $I_2 = 1~\mu\text{A}$ and $R_1 = 1~\text{k}\Omega$.

Solution

$$I_2 R_1 = (1~\mu\text{A})(1~\text{k}\Omega) = 1~\text{mV}.$$

Thus, we can say that a $1\mu A$ bias current flowing through a 1 kΩ resistor produces the same effect as a 1 mV offset voltage.

Recall that we omitted resistor R_2 in the preceding discussion. We know that the actual inverting amplifier appears as shown in Figure 6-13(a).

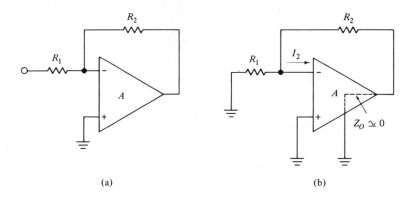

(a)   (b)

Figure 6-13

Exact Circuit for Computing Offset Due to Bias Currents

Refer now to Figure 6-13(b). Note that we have set the source voltage equal to zero. It can be seen from Figure 6-13(b) that bias current I_2 flows through both resistor R_1 *and* resistor R_2. Note that the right-hand terminal of R_2 is connected to the output terminal of the amplifier. If the value of the dc output impedance of the op amp is approximately equal to zero, there is practically no impedance between the right-hand terminal of R_2 and ground. Thus, we can say that resistors R_1 and R_2 are effectively connected in *parallel* when the source voltage is equal to zero, as in Figure 6-13(b). Therefore, the *actual* equivalent offset voltage for the inverting amplifier is equal to the product of bias current I_2 and the parallel equivalent of resistors R_1 and R_2:

$$I_2\left(\frac{R_1 R_2}{R_1 + R_2}\right) = \text{the equivalent offset voltage.}$$

Naturally we should like to eliminate or minimize this equivalent offset voltage. We cannot, however, eliminate bias current I_2 because its presence is necessary for proper biasing of the op amp transistor stages. Nor can we eliminate resistors R_1 and R_2 since they provide us with a stable gain. What shall we do? We again move to *cancel* the effect of the equivalent offset voltage. This is accomplished by inserting a resistor, R', between the plus terminal of the op amp and ground, as shown in Figure 6-14. The current flowing through R' is bias current I_1. Thus, we can express the value of V_{I_1} as follows:

$$V_{I_1} = -I_1 R'. \tag{6-20}$$

We also know that V_{I_2} is given by the following expression:

$$V_{I_2} = -I_2\left(\frac{R_1 R_2}{R_1 + R_2}\right). \tag{6-21}$$

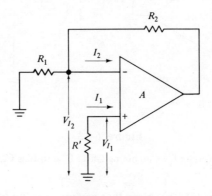

Figure 6-14

Compensation for Bias Currents

We may now substitute into Equation (6-7) to determine the value of the output voltage, V_O.

$$V_O = A(V_{I_1} - V_{I_2}), \tag{6-7}$$

$$V_O = A\left[-I_1 R' - \left(-I_2\frac{R_1 R_2}{R_1 + R_2}\right)\right], \tag{6-22}$$

$$V_O = A\left[I_2\left(\frac{R_1 R_2}{R_1 + R_2}\right) - I_1 R'\right]. \tag{6-23}$$

Note that the value of the output voltage is directly proportional to the difference between two terms. This difference is equal to the equivalent offset voltage for the circuit of Figure 6-14.

$$I_2\left(\frac{R_1 R_2}{R_1 + R_2}\right) - I_1 R' = \text{the equivalent offset voltage.}$$

To cancel the effect of the equivalent offset voltage, we merely set these two terms equal to each other, as follows:

$$I_2\left(\frac{R_1 R_2}{R_1 + R_2}\right) = I_1 R'. \tag{6-24}$$

If bias currents I_1 and I_2 are equal, we may write the following:

$$\frac{R_1 R_2}{R_1 + R_2} = R'. \tag{6-25}$$

Equation (6-25) says that we must set the value of R' equal to the parallel equivalent of resistors R_1 and R_2 in order to cancel the effect of the equivalent offset voltage. If we set R' equal to the value specified by Equation (6-25), we may express the equivalent offset voltage as follows:

$$I_2 R' - I_1 R' = R'(I_2 - I_1) = \text{the equivalent offset voltage.} \tag{6-26}$$

For $I_1 = I_2$: the equivalent offset voltage = 0.

Thus, the inclusion of resistor R' in the circuit of Figure 6-14 appears to result in the cancellation of the effect of the equivalent offset voltage

Due to manufacturing limitations, however, the two input stages of the op amp will never be identical. This means that the two bias currents, I_1 and I_2, will generally *not* be equal. We now define a new term known as I_{OS}, the *offset* current, or *difference* current. This is equal to the difference between the two bias currents:

$$\boldsymbol{I_{OS} = I_1 - I_2 = \textbf{the offset (difference) current.}} \tag{6-27}$$

We may now express the equivalent offset voltage as follows:

$$R'(I_2 - I_1) = R' I_{OS} = \text{the equivalent offset voltage.} \tag{6-28}$$

We shall soon see that this equivalent offset voltage can be adjusted to zero at room temperature. However, like V_{OS}, I_{OS} drifts with temperature. We shall study the effects of both V_{OS} and I_{OS} in the next section.

6-5   The Error Voltage

We are now ready to discuss the performance of a dc amplifier. In particular, we are interested in the effects of both offset and drift on this performance. The complete circuit of the inverting feedback amplifier is shown in Figure 6-15(a). For ease of manipulation, we shall replace the compensating circuit (R_X, R_Y, and R_Z) by its Thevenin equivalent, as shown in Figure 6-15(b). In this circuit, V_C is the Thevenin voltage and R_C is the Thevenin resistance. Strictly speaking, R_C is in series with R'. However, the value of R_C is generally much smaller than that of R', and thus, can be neglected.

We should like to obtain an expression for the dc output voltage, V_O, for the circuit of Figure 6-15. The derivation of such an expression is quite involved. The resulting equation may be written as follows:

$$V_O = \left(-\frac{R_2}{R_1}V_S\right) + \left[\frac{R_1 + R_2}{R_1}(V_C - V_{OS}) + R_2 I_{OS}\right]. \qquad (6\text{-}29)$$

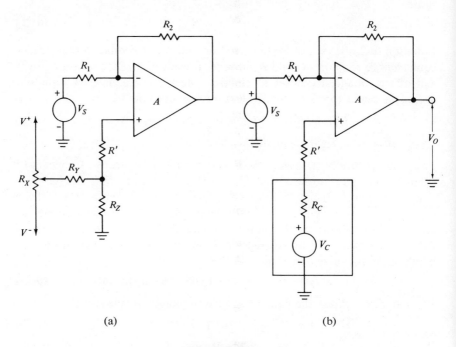

(a)   (b)

Figure 6-15

Completely Compensated Amplifier

Note that the right-hand side of the equation is composed of two major terms. The first term, $(-R_2/R_1)V_S$, is directly proportional to the source voltage. The second term depends upon the values of both V_{OS} and I_{OS}. This term represents an *error* in the output voltage due to the presence of offset. Ideally, of course, we should like the error term to be equal to zero. Note that this error term contains V_C, the Thevenin voltage of the compensating circuit. Let us set the error term in Equation (6-29) equal to zero and solve for V_C.

$$\left(\frac{R_1 + R_2}{R_1}\right)(V_C - V_{OS}) + R_2 I_{OS} = 0, \qquad (6\text{-}30)$$

$$V_C = V_{OS} - \left(\frac{R_1 R_2}{R_1 + R_2}\right)I_{OS}. \qquad (6\text{-}31)$$

Equation (6-31) indicates the necessary conditions for the cancellation of the error. The equation merely predicts that error cancellation is a mathematical possibility. In practice, we "null" the amplifier *experimentally* by varying the position of the potentiometer wiper (and hence the value of V_C) until a digital voltmeter connected across the output terminals reads zero (see Section 6-2 and Figure 6-10). Thus, we see that the effects of both V_{OS} and I_{OS} can be cancelled by making use of the potentiometer arrangement shown in Figure 6-15(a).

It was mentioned previously that the amplifier is nulled at room temperature (25°C). Let us assume now that the amplifier has been nulled; that is, the error at room temperature is equal to zero. We know that the values of both V_{OS} and I_{OS} drift with temperature. A glance at Equation (6-29) reveals that any change in the values of V_{OS} and I_{OS} results in a change in the error, which in turn causes a change in the output voltage. Therefore, at temperatures *other than* 25°C, the error will *not* be equal to zero. Here lies the problem. The potentiometer is adjusted for error cancellation only *once*, at room temperature. However, the variation in V_{OS} and I_{OS} with temperature results in a finite error at all temperatures other than 25°C. Thus, we see again that it is drift, not initial offset, which is the major problem.

In order to determine the effect of drift upon amplifier performance, we must define a new term known as the *rate of change of output voltage with temperature.*

$$\frac{\Delta V_O}{\Delta T} = \text{the rate of change of output voltage with temperature.}$$

We can express this rate of change by applying elementary calculus to Equation (6-29).

$$\frac{\Delta V_O}{\Delta T} = -\left(\frac{R_1 + R_2}{R_1}\right)\left(\frac{\Delta V_{OS}}{\Delta T}\right) + R_2\left(\frac{\Delta I_{OS}}{\Delta T}\right). \tag{6-32}$$

Note that the rate of change of the output voltage depends upon both voltage and current drift. Recall that the value of drift can be either positive or negative. Therefore, depending upon the *signs* of the voltage and current drift, the two effects may tend either to *cancel* each other, or to *reinforce* each other. Since the behavior of drift can be quite erratic (see Section 6-3), we have no choice but to assume that the two effects are *cumulative.* In other words, we shall treat the problem as a worst case situation. We can rewrite Equation (6-32) as follows:

$$\frac{\Delta V_O}{\Delta T} = \left(\frac{R_1 + R_2}{R_1}\right)\left|\frac{\Delta V_{OS}}{\Delta T}\right| + R_2\left|\frac{\Delta I_{OS}}{\Delta T}\right|. \tag{6-33}$$

Equation (6-33) says that we shall disregard signs and consider only the *absolute values* of the voltage and current drift. This equation gives the maximum value of the rate of change of the output voltage. For simplicity, we shall omit the absolute value signs from this point on.

We now define a term called the *error voltage, E*. This is equal to the change in output voltage resulting from a change in temperature.

$$E = \Delta V_O = \text{the error voltage.} \qquad (6\text{-}34)$$

The error voltage may also be expressed as follows:

$$E = \Delta V_O = \left(\frac{\Delta V_O}{\Delta T}\right)(\Delta T). \qquad (6\text{-}35)$$

In Equation (6-35), ΔT represents the change in temperature *from 25°C*. Substituting Equation (6-33) into Equation (6-35), we get

$$E = \left(\frac{R_1 + R_2}{R_1}\right)\left(\frac{\Delta V_{OS}}{\Delta T}\right)(\Delta T) + R_2\left(\frac{\Delta I_{OS}}{\Delta T}\right)(\Delta T). \qquad (6\text{-}36)$$

Finally, we may express the output voltage, V_O, as follows:

$$V_O = -\frac{R_2}{R_1}(V_S) + E. \qquad (6\text{-}37)$$

$$\underset{\text{Ideal}}{\uparrow} \qquad \underset{\text{Error}}{\uparrow}$$

Equation (6-37) says that the output voltage is composed of two terms, an *ideal* voltage and an *error* voltage. The ideal voltage is directly proportional to the source voltage, V_S. The error voltage depends upon the voltage and current drift, and the temperature change. Ideally, of course, we should like the error voltage to be equal to zero. An examination of Equation (6-36) reveals that the error voltage would be equal to zero if the values of both the voltage and current drift were zero. This is impossible because all practical op amps have finite values of drift. Equation (6-36) also says that the error voltage would be equal to zero if the temperature change, ΔT, were zero. This is impractical because the amplifier is frequently placed in environments where the temperature *does* change. Thus, all dc amplifiers exhibit some finite error resulting from drift. What effect does this error have upon the performance of the dc amplifier? This question will be answered in the following examples.

EXAMPLE 6-6

The following data are given for a dc amplifier:

Op Amp	Feedback Network	Source
$\dfrac{\Delta V_{OS}}{\Delta T} = 10 \ \mu\text{V}/°\text{C}$	$R_1 = 1 \ \text{k}\Omega$	$V_S = 100 \ \text{mV dc}$
$\dfrac{\Delta I_{OS}}{\Delta T} = 10 \ \text{nA}/°\text{C}$	$R_2 = 10 \ \text{k}\Omega$	

The amplifier is nulled at room temperature. Compute the value of the output voltage at 125°C.

Solution

Let us first compute the value of the error voltage, E. The change in temperature, ΔT, is equal to 100°C (125 minus 25). Substituting into Equation (6-36), we get

$$E = \left(\frac{R_1 + R_2}{R_1}\right)\left(\frac{\Delta V_{OS}}{\Delta T}\right)(\Delta T) + R_2\left(\frac{\Delta I_{OS}}{\Delta T}\right)(\Delta T),$$

$$E = \left(\frac{1 + 10}{1}\right)(10 \ \mu\text{V}/°\text{C})(100°\text{C}) + (10 \ \text{k}\Omega)(10 \ \text{nA}/°\text{C})(100°\text{C}) = 21 \ \text{mV}.$$

We now substitute into Equation (6-37) to determine the value of V_O.

$$V_O = -\frac{R_2}{R_1}(V_S) + E,$$

$$V_O = -\left(\frac{10 \ \text{k}\Omega}{1 \ \text{k}\Omega}\right)(100 \ \text{mV}) + 21 \ \text{mV},$$

$$V_O = -1000 \ \text{mV} + 21 \ \text{mV}.$$
$$\underset{\text{Ideal}}{\uparrow} \qquad\qquad \underset{\text{Error}}{\uparrow}$$

Note that the ideal output voltage is equal to -1000 mV while the error voltage is equal to 21 mV. This gives a percentage error of 2.1 percent. Strictly speaking, the error voltage may be either positive or negative. This means that the output voltage can vary between -979 mV (-1000 mV *plus* 21 mV) and -1021 mV (-1000 mV *minus* 21 mV) as the temperature varies between 25°C and 125°C. We can summarize the results of Example 6-6 as follows:

Ideal output voltage = −1000 mV
Error voltage = ±21 mV
Percentage error = 2.1 percent
Range of output voltage: −979 mV to −1021 mV

Can an error of 2.1 percent be tolerated in a dc amplifier? The answer to this question depends upon the particular application for which the amplifier is intended.

EXAMPLE 6-7

Repeat Example 6-6, except make V_S = 10 mV.

Solution

A glance at Equation (6-36) reveals that the error voltage depends upon the values of the feedback resistors, the voltage and current drift, and the temperature change. Since none of these factors has changed, the value of the error voltage is still equal to 21 mV. Substituting into Equation (6-37), we get

$$V_O = −R_2(V_S) + E,$$

$$V_O = −\left(\frac{10 \text{ k}\Omega}{1 \text{ k}\Omega}\right)(10 \text{ mV}) + 21 \text{ mV}.$$

$$V_O = −100 \text{ mV} + 21 \text{ mV}.$$

Note that the ideal output voltage is equal to −100 mV while the error voltage is equal to 21 mV. This gives a percentage error of 21 percent. The output voltage can vary between −79 mV and −121 mV as the temperature varies between 25°C and 125°C. We can summarize the results of Example 6-7 as follows:

Ideal output voltage = −100 mV
Error voltage = ±21 mV
Percentage error = 21 percent
Range of output voltage: −79 mV to −121 mV

Now, let us compare the results of Example 6-6 and Example 6-7. The error voltage (21 mV) is the *same* in both examples. This is so because the same feedback resistors, the same op amp (same voltage and current drift), and the same temperature change were used in both examples. However, we amplified a *smaller* source voltage in Example 6-7 (10 mV) than in Example

6-6 (100 mV). This means that the ideal output voltage in Example 6-7 (-100 mV) was *smaller* than in Example 6-6 (-1000 mV). Therefore, the percentage error was *larger* in Example 6-7 (21 percent) than in Example 6-6 (2.1 percent). Here is a very important point. Since the error voltage is *fixed* for a given amplifier, we can say that the percentage error is *inversely* proportional to the value of the input signal (V_S). What does this mean? It means that for a given op amp and temperature change, the percentage error will increase as we try to amplify smaller and smaller signals. In other words, the *error voltage limits the size of the smallest dc signal which can be amplified accurately.* Can we improve the accuracy? The answer is yes. We can replace the op amp with one which has smaller values of voltage and current drift.

EXAMPLE 6-8

Repeat Example 6-7, except use an op amp whose voltage drift is 1 μV/°C and whose current drift is 1 nA/°C.

Solution

We now have a new op amp, which means that we have different values of voltage and current drift. Thus, the value of the error voltage will change.

$$E = \left(\frac{R_1 + R_2}{R_1}\right)\left(\frac{\Delta V_{OS}}{\Delta T}\right)(\Delta T) + R_2\left(\frac{\Delta I_{OS}}{\Delta T}\right)(\Delta T),$$

$$E = \left(\frac{1 + 10}{1}\right)(1 \ \mu V/°C)(100°C) + (10 \ k\Omega)(1 \ nA/°C)(100°C) = 2.1 \ mV.$$

Note that the use of an op amp with smaller values of drift has resulted in a large reduction in the value of the error voltage (from 21 mV to 2.1 mV). The value of the output voltage is

$$V_O = -\frac{R_2}{R_1}(V_S) + E,$$

$$V_O = -\left(\frac{10 \ k\Omega}{1 \ k\Omega}\right)(10 \ mV) + 2.1 \ mV,$$

$$V_O = -100 \ mV + 2.1 \ mV.$$

Note that the ideal output voltage is equal to -100 mV while the error voltage is equal to 2.1 mV. This gives a percentage error of 2.1 percent. The output voltage can vary between -97.9 mV and -102.1 mV as the temperature varies between 25°C and 125°C. We can summarize the results of Example 6-8 as follows:

Ideal output voltage = −100 mV
Error voltage = ±2.1 mV
Percentage error = 2.1 percent
Range of output voltage: −97.9 mV to −102.1 mV

Comparing the results of Example 6-8 with those of Example 6-7, we see that the value of the ideal output voltage is the same (−100 mV). This is so because the value of the input source voltage is the same (10 mV). In Example 6-8, however, we used an op amp having very small values of voltage and current drift. This resulted in a reduction of the error voltage from 21 mV to 2.1 mV, which in turn improved the accuracy from 21 percent to 2.1 percent. Thus, we see that for a given value of source voltage, we can improve the accuracy by reducing the drift.

The results of the preceding examples can be illustrated graphically. Equation (6-37) is actually the equation of a straight line, as shown:

$$V_O = \left(-\frac{R_2}{R_1}\right)V_S + E, \tag{6-37}$$

$$y = (m)X + b.$$

Equating terms, we can write the following:

$$b = V_O\text{-intercept} = E \text{ (the error voltage)}, \tag{6-38}$$

$$m = \text{slope} = -\frac{R_2}{R_1} \text{ (the ideal closed loop gain)}. \tag{6-39}$$

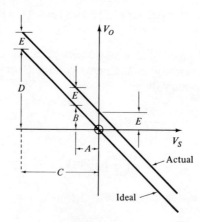

Figure 6-16

Graphical Representation of Error Voltage

Two curves of output voltage, V_O, versus source voltage, V_S, are shown in Figure 6-16. The *ideal* curve passes through the origin (error voltage equal to zero). The *actual* curve does *not* pass through the origin (error voltage is finite). Since the V_O-intercept is equal to the error voltage, the *vertical* distance between the two curves is constant and equal to E. We can now illustrate the effect of the error voltage on the amplifier performance. Suppose that the value of the source voltage is equal to A, as shown in Figure 6-16. In this case, the value of the ideal output voltage is equal to B. Note that the error voltage, E, is not very small in comparison with B, and thus, the percentage error will be relatively large. Suppose, on the other hand, that the value of the source voltage is equal to C. In this case, the value of the ideal output voltage is equal to D. Note that the error voltage, E, is relatively small in comparison with D, and thus, the percentage error will be much smaller. We see again that the error voltage limits the size of the smallest dc signal which can be amplified accurately.

6-6   The Error Voltage Referred to the Input

We shall now present a simple technique that can be used to determine the accuracy of a dc amplifier. We know that the value of the output voltage V_O, of the inverting dc amplifier is given by Equation (6-37).

$$V_O = -\frac{R_2}{R_1}(V_S) + E. \qquad (6\text{-}37)$$

We now define a term known as the *error voltage referred to the input*, E_I.

E_I = **the error voltage referred to the input.**

E_I is the value of source voltage, V_S, at which the output voltage is equal to zero. We can determine this value quite simply by making use of Equation (6-37). We merely substitute $V_O = 0$ and solve for V_S as follows:

$$V_O = 0 = -\frac{R_2}{R_1}(V_S) + E, \qquad (6\text{-}40)$$

$$V_S = \frac{R_1}{R_2}(E), \qquad (6\text{-}41)$$

$$E_I = \frac{R_1}{R_2}(E). \qquad (6\text{-}42)$$

Equation (6-42) gives the relationship between the error voltage referred to the input, E_I, and the error voltage, E. We can rewrite Equation (6-42) as follows:

$$E = \frac{R_2}{R_1}(E_I). \qquad (6\text{-}43)$$

Note that E is equal to E_I multiplied by the ideal closed loop gain of the inverting feedback amplifier (R_2/R_1).

We can obtain a more useful expression for the output voltage by rewriting Equation (6-37) as follows:

$$V_O = -\frac{R_2}{R_1}(V_S) + E, \tag{6-37}$$

$$V_O = -\frac{R_2}{R_1}(V_S) + \frac{R_2}{R_1}(E_I), \tag{6-44}$$

$$V_O = -\frac{R_2}{R_1}(V_S - E_I). \tag{6-45}$$

Note that Equation (6-45) contains the term $(V_S - E_I)$. This says that we can consider E_I to be a voltage generator connected in series with V_S, as shown in Figure 6-17. Is E_I a physical generator which is actually connected

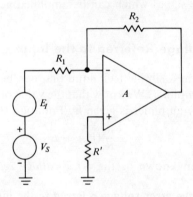

Figure 6-17

Equivalent Circuit Containing Error Voltage Referred to the Input

in the circuit? No, it is not. We merely indicate its presence in the circuit diagram in order to account for the effect of errors caused by drift. E_I is an *unwanted* generator; that is, it gets amplified along with V_S whether we like it or not. In other words, instead of accounting for drift errors by an error voltage, E, generated at the amplifier *output*, we shall refer the error to the *input* terminals. We can obtain an expression for E_I for the inverting amplifier by substituting Equation (6-36) into Equation (6-42).

$$E_I = \frac{R_1}{R_2}E = \frac{R_1}{R_2}\left[\left(\frac{R_1 + R_2}{R_1}\right)\left(\frac{\Delta V_{OS}}{\Delta T}\right)(\Delta T) + R_2\left(\frac{\Delta I_{OS}}{\Delta T}\right)(\Delta T)\right]. \tag{6-46}$$

$$E_I = \left(\frac{R_1 + R_2}{R_2}\right)\left(\frac{\Delta V_{OS}}{\Delta T}\right)(\Delta T) + R_1\left(\frac{\Delta I_{OS}}{\Delta T}\right)(\Delta T). \tag{6-47}$$

The nice thing about dealing with E_I is that the determination of the percentage error becomes relatively simple. The procedure is as follows:

1. Compute the value of E_I.
2. Compare the value of E_I with that of V_S.
3. Compute the percentage error as $(E_I/V_S)(100)$.

EXAMPLE 6-9

Compute the percentage error in Example 6-6 using the aforementioned technique.

Solution

We first compute the value of E_I.

$$E_I = \left(\frac{R_1 + R_2}{R_2}\right)\left(\frac{\Delta V_{OS}}{\Delta T}\right)(\Delta T) + R_1\left(\frac{\Delta I_{OS}}{\Delta T}\right)(\Delta T),$$

$$E_I = \left(\frac{1 + 10}{10}\right)(10 \ \mu V/°C)(100°C) + 1 \ k\Omega(10 \ nA/°C)(100°C) = 2.1 \ mV.$$

The percentage error is:

$$\text{Percentage error} = \frac{E_I}{V_S}(100) = \frac{2.1 \ mV}{100 \ mV}(100) = 2.1 \ \text{percent.}$$

This is the same answer we obtained in Example 6-6. Thus, we see that the percentage error is directly proportional to the value of the error voltage referred to the input, E_I, and inversely proportional to the value of the source voltage, V_S.

For a given value of V_S, the accuracy can be improved only by reducing the value of E_I. Let us see how this is done. A glance at Equation (6-47) reveals that the expression for E_I is composed of two terms. The first term is

$$\left(\frac{R_1 + R_2}{R_2}\right)\left(\frac{\Delta V_{OS}}{\Delta T}\right)(\Delta T) = \left(1 + \frac{R_1}{R_2}\right)\left(\frac{\Delta V_{OS}}{\Delta T}\right)(\Delta T).$$

Since the value of the ideal closed loop gain is equal to $-(R_2/R_1)$, the ratio (R_1/R_2) is generally much smaller than one, and thus, its effect upon the value of the first term is negligible. Therefore, the only way to reduce the value of the first term is to obtain an op amp which has a small value of voltage drift. The second term is

$$R_1\left(\frac{\Delta I_{OS}}{\Delta T}\right)(\Delta T).$$

Note that the value of the second term is directly proportional to the value of R_1. Thus, we should like to keep the value of R_1 small. We saw in

Chapter 5, however, that a small value of R_1 loads down the source. Therefore, if high accuracy is required, we use a small value of R_1 and insert a buffer between the source and the amplifier.

6-7   Drift in ac Amplifiers

We have been discussing the effects of drift upon the performance of dc amplifiers. While these effects are most pronounced in dc amplifiers, they can also cause serious problems in ac amplifiers. Refer now to the following examples.

EXAMPLE 6-10

The following data are given for an ac amplifier:

Op Amp	Feedback Network	Source
$V_S{}^+ = V_S{}^- = 15$ V	$R_1 = 10$ kΩ	$V_S =$ a 0.5 V peak sine wave
$\dfrac{\Delta V_{os}}{\Delta T} = 10 \ \mu V/°C$	$R_2 = 140$ kΩ	
$\dfrac{\Delta I_{os}}{\Delta T} = 200$ nA/°C		

The amplifier is nulled at room temperature.

   (a) Sketch the waveform of the output voltage, V_O, at room temperature.
   (b) Sketch the waveform of the output voltage, V_O, at 125°C.

Solution

   (a) $T = 25°C$ (room temperature)

We shall assume that the value of the loop gain is large enough so that the closed loop gain of the amplifier is approximately equal to its *ideal*

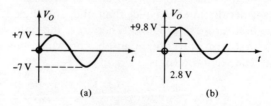

(a)   (b)

Figure 6-18

Drift in ac Amplifiers

value, namely $-(R_2/R_1)$. Omitting the minus sign for simplicity, we can write the following:

$$V_O = \frac{R_2}{R_1}(V_S) = \frac{140 \text{ k}\Omega}{10 \text{ k}\Omega}(0.5 \text{ V}) = 7 \text{ V}.$$

The output voltage is a sine wave having a peak value of 7 V. Since the amplifier has been nulled at room temperature, there is no dc error voltage at the output. Thus, the waveform of the output voltage is a 7 V peak sine wave "riding" on a 0 V dc level, as shown in Figure 6-18(a).

(b) $T = 125°C$

As the temperature changes, both the voltage and current offset drift. Thus, the error voltage is finite at 125°C. The value of this error voltage is

$$E = \left(\frac{R_1 + R_2}{R_1}\right)\left(\frac{\Delta V_{OS}}{\Delta T}\right)(\Delta T) + R_2\left(\frac{\Delta I_{OS}}{\Delta T}\right)(\Delta T),$$

$$E = \left(\frac{10 + 140}{10}\right)(10 \text{ } \mu\text{V}/°\text{C})(100°\text{C}) + 140 \text{ k}\Omega(200 \text{ nA}/°\text{C})(100°\text{C}) \simeq 2.8 \text{ V}.$$

The input voltage is a "pure" sine wave; that is, it rides on a 0 V dc level. The dc output voltage, however, can be as large as ± 2.8 V even though the dc input voltage is zero. Therefore, the 7 V peak sine wave at the output now rides on a 2.8 V dc level, as shown in Figure 6-18(b). In other words, the entire sine wave has been *shifted* up (or down) by 2.8 V. The peak value of the ac output voltage, however, is still equal to 7 V (9.8 V minus 2.8 V). Since we are interested only in the *ac* output voltage, no damage has been done by the dc level shift resulting from amplifier drift.

EXAMPLE 6-11

Repeat Example 6-10, except make $V_S = $ a 1 V peak sine wave.

Solution

(a) $T = 25°C$

The peak value of the ac output voltage is

$$V_O = \frac{R_2}{R_1}(V_S) = \frac{140 \text{ k}\Omega}{10 \text{ k}\Omega}(1 \text{ V}) = 14 \text{ V}.$$

The waveform of the output voltage is a 14 V peak sine wave riding on a 0 V dc level, as shown in Figure 6-19(a).

(b) $T = 125°C$

At $T = 125°C$, there is a finite dc error voltage at the output equal to 2.8 V. Thus, the output sine wave will be shifted up or down by 2.8 V. Assuming an upward shift, the maximum positive value of the output

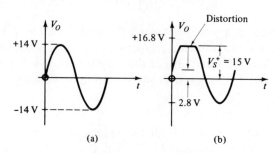

Figure 6-19

Distortion Caused by Drift in ac Amplifiers

voltage will *try* to increase to $+16.8$ V (14 V plus 2.8 V), as shown in Figure 6-19(b). However, the amplifier *saturates* at $V_O = +15$ V, and thus, the output waveform becomes distorted. We see, then, that the dc level shift at the output can result in distortion if the amplitude of the ac output voltage is close to the saturation value.

6-8   Drift in the Noninverting Amplifier

Throughout this chapter, we have discussed the effects of drift on the performance of an inverting amplifier. The same problems manifest themselves in the noninverting amplifier. The complete circuit for the noninverting dc amplifier is shown in Figure 6-20. Note that a resistor, R'_S, is connected in series with the minus input terminal of the op amp. This resistor is used to cancel the effect of offset current. The value of R_S (the resistive portion of the source impedance, Z_S) is compared with that of the parallel equivalent of R_1 and R_2 (neglecting the Thevenin resistance of the compensating circuit). It can be shown that if the value of R_S is larger than that of the parallel equivalent, R'_S is connected as shown and its value is selected such that

$$R_S = R_S' + \frac{R_1 R_2}{R_1 + R_2}. \tag{6-48}$$

If, on the other hand, the value of R_S is smaller than that of the parallel equivalent, R'_S is connected in series with R_S and its value is selected such that

$$R_S + R_S' = \frac{R_1 R_2}{R_1 + R_2}. \tag{6-49}$$

It can be shown that the expression for the dc output voltage, V_O, of the noninverting amplifier is

$$V_O = \left(\frac{R_1 + R_2}{R_2}\right)V_S + E, \tag{6-50}$$

$$V_O = \left(\frac{R_1 + R_2}{R_2}\right)(V_S + E_I). \tag{6-51}$$

The value of E_I is given by

$$E_I = \left(\frac{\Delta V_{OS}}{\Delta T}\right)(\Delta T) + R_S\left(\frac{\Delta I_{OS}}{\Delta T}\right)(\Delta T). \tag{6-52}$$

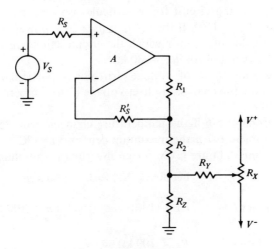

Figure 6-20

Completely Compensated Noninverting Feedback Amplifier

SUMMARY

1. All practical op amps have finite values of offset voltage and current.
2. The amplifier can be nulled at room temperature by means of a potentiometer circuit.
3. Both the voltage and current offset drift with temperature. This drift results in a finite error voltage at temperatures other than 25°C.
4. Since the error voltage is fixed for a given amplifier and temperature change, it limits the size of the smallest dc signal which can be amplified accurately.
5. The error voltage referred to the input can be compared with the source voltage to determine the accuracy.

6. A change in temperature shifts the dc level of the output waveform. This can result in distortion when the amplitude of the ac output voltage is close to the saturation value.

PROBLEMS

6-1.   The manufacturer of a particular op amp specifies that the maximum offset voltage at room temperature is ± 3 mV. The op amp uses 15 V power supplies. Design the compensating circuit.

6-2.   Repeat Problem 6-1 for $V_{OS} = \pm 5$ mV.

6-3.   Repeat Problem 6-2 if the op amp uses 12 V power supplies.

6-4.   The compensating circuit for a particular op amp has $R_X = 10$ kΩ, $R_Y = 40$ kΩ, and $R_Z = 15$ Ω. If the op amp uses 20 V power supplies, what is the maximum value of V_{OS} for which the circuit can correct?

6-5.   Repeat Problem 6-4 for $R_X = 80$ kΩ.

6-6.   The maximum value of voltage drift for a particular op amp is 15 μV/°C. Compute the change in offset voltage if the temperature changes from 25°C to 40°C.

6-7.   Repeat Problem 6-6 if the temperature changes from 25°C to 95°C.

6-8.   Repeat Problem 6-7 if the maximum drift is 5 μV/°C.

6-9.   The following data are given for an inverting dc amplifier:

Op Amp	Feedback Network	Source
$\dfrac{\Delta V_{OS}}{\Delta T} = 15\ \mu\text{V}/°\text{C}$	$R_1 = 1$ kΩ	$V_S = 100$ mV dc
$\dfrac{\Delta I_{OS}}{\Delta T} = 12\ \text{nA}/°\text{C}$	$R_2 = 100$ kΩ	

The amplifier is nulled at room temperature. The temperature varies between 25°C and 85°C.

(a) Compute the value of the ideal output voltage.
(b) Compute the value of the error voltage.
(c) Compute the value of the percentage error.
(d) What is the range of the output voltage?

6-10.   Repeat Problem 6-9, except make $V_S = 10$ mV dc. Compare the results with those of Problem 6-9 and explain.

6-11.   Repeat Problem 6-9, except make $V_S = 1$ mV dc. Compare the results with those of Problem 6-10 and explain.

6-12.   Repeat Problem 6-11, except change the op amp to one whose voltage drift is 2 μV/°C and whose current drift is 5 nA/°C. Explain why the percentage error is smaller in Problem 6-12 than in Problem 6-11.

6-13.   It is desired that the amplifier of Problem 6-9 be used to amplify a 50 mV dc voltage in an enviromnent where the temperature varies between 25°C and 55°C. The percentage error is not to exceed 1 percent. Does the amplifier meet the specification?

6-14.(a) Compute the value of E_I for the amplifier of Problem 6-9.

(b) Compute the percentage error by comparing E_I with V_S.

(c) Compare the answer to part (b) with that of Problem 6-9, part (c).

6-15. The following data are given for an inverting amplifier:

Op Amp	Feedback Network	Source
$V_S{}^+ = V_S{}^- = 10$ V	$R_1 = 10$ kΩ	$V_S = $ a 1 V peak sine wave
$\dfrac{\Delta V_{os}}{\Delta I} = 20 \,\mu\text{V}/°\text{C}$	$R_2 = 90$ kΩ	
$\dfrac{\Delta I_{os}}{\Delta T} = 200 \text{ nA}/°\text{C}$		

The amplifier is nulled at room temperature.

(a) Sketch the waveform of the output voltage, V_O, at room temperature.

(b) Sketch the waveform of the output voltage, V_O, at 125°C.

6-16. Repeat Problem 6-15, except make $R_1 = 1$ kΩ and $R_2 = 9$ kΩ. Compare the results with those of Problem 6-15 and explain.

7

Frequency Response

Just as the last chapter was devoted to the study of dc amplifiers, this chapter deals with ac amplifiers. In our previous discussions, we said nothing about the frequency of the ac input signal to the amplifier. You may have gotten the impression that the gain of the amplifier is the same at all frequencies. This, unfortunately, is not the case. Due to certain aspects of the circuitry within the op amp, the gain decreases as the frequency increases. This variation in op amp gain with frequency imposes severe limitations upon both the use and the performance of the device. In this chapter, we shall study the factors responsible for these variations as well as their effect upon the performance of the amplifier. In other words, we shall discuss the *frequency response* of the op amp, or the manner in which the op amp *responds* to different frequencies. Finally, we shall deal with the effect of the incorporation of negative feedback upon the performance of the amplifier.

7-1 The High-Frequency Equivalent Circuit

Throughout this text, we have been treating the op amp as a single unit. We know, however, that it is the nature of the circuitry within the device that determines its behavior. For example, we have seen that the performance of the amplifier depends to some degree upon such factors as input impedance, output impedance, gain, common-mode rejection ratio, offset, and drift. Therefore, we can say that everything inside the op amp affects its behavior in some way.

We saw in Chapter 3 that the op amp is actually a multistage transistor amplifier. A glance at Figure 3-1 reveals that this amplifier is composed of transistors and resistors. Therefore, whether the op amp is a discrete, hybrid, or *IC*, its interior has conducting paths separated by insulators from other conducting paths. Whenever two conductors are separated by an insulator, the resultant effect is as though a *capacitor* were present. What does this mean? It means that the interior of the op amp contains a number of capacitors. But why are there no capacitors indicated in the circuit schematic of Figure 3-1? The answer is that these capacitors are "uninvited guests." In other words, they have not been intentionally included in the op amp. Their presence is an unavoidable result of the construction of the device. The capacitive effects stem from two major sources:

1. There are capacitors within the transistors resulting from the physical characteristics of semiconductor materials.
2. There are *stray* capacitances formed by the separation of conducting paths by insulators.

It is the presence of these capacitors which causes the reduction of the op amp gain at high frequencies, as we shall now see.

In order to illustrate the effect of the capacitors upon the operation of the op amp, we must introduce the *high-frequency* equivalent circuit. This circuit is shown in Figure 7-1. Note that we are considering the behavior of the op amp itself (no feedback). Reference to Figure 7-1 reveals that the high-frequency equivalent circuit of the op amp is composed of three entities:

1. A controlled voltage generator, $A_L V_I$
2. A resistor, R
3. A capacitor, C

We are assuming, for the moment, that there is just *one* capacitor within the op amp. Actually, the equivalent circuit is considerably more complex than shown in Figure 7-1; that is, it contains a relatively large number of resistors and capacitors. We have simplified the circuit to the extent shown in the figure (one generator, one resistor, and one capacitor) in order to illustrate some important concepts.

We shall now present a qualitative discussion of the behavior of the circuit of Figure 7-1. Note that the circuit contains a voltage divider composed of R and C. At low frequencies, the value of the capacitive reactance, X_C, is relatively large. If X_C is much larger than R, the voltage

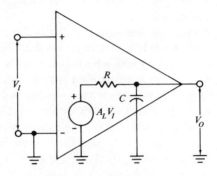

Figure 7-1

High-Frequency Equivalent Circuit of Op Amp

across the capacitor (which is also the output voltage) is approximately equal to the value of the controlled generator voltage, $A_L V_I$. As the frequency increases, X_C decreases. Eventually, a frequency will be reached where the value of X_C is no longer much larger than R. At this frequency, the value of the output voltage will be *less* than $A_L V_I$. As the frequency continues to *increase*, X_C, and hence V_O, continue to *decrease*. If the input voltage, V_I, remains constant, a decrease in the output voltage, V_O, is an indication of the fact that the gain, A, of the op amp is decreasing. Thus, we see that the presence of the capacitor is responsible for the reduction of the op amp gain at high frequencies.

Now, let us obtain an expression for the gain of the op amp. We know that the gain may be expressed as follows:

$$A = \frac{V_O}{V_I}.$$

Utilizing the circuit of Figure 7-1, we can rewrite the expression as follows:

$$A = \frac{V_O}{V_I} = \frac{\dfrac{(A_L V_I)(-jX_C)}{R - jX_C}}{V_I} = \frac{A_L}{1 + j2\pi fRC}. \tag{7-1}$$

Let us define a specific frequency, f_1, as follows:

$$f_1 = \frac{1}{2\pi RC}. \tag{7-2}$$

Substituting this expression into Equation (7-1), we get the following:

$$A = \frac{A_L}{1 + j\frac{f}{f_1}},\tag{7-3}$$

$$A = \frac{A_L}{\sqrt{1 + \left(\frac{f}{f_1}\right)^2}} \Big/ -\arctan\left(\frac{f}{f_1}\right).\tag{7-4}$$

A_L and f_1 are defined as follows:

A_L = **the low-frequency gain,**

f_1 = **the corner frequency.**

Notice in Equation (7-4) that f is a *variable* that can represent any value of frequency, whereas f_1 is a *specific* frequency that depends upon the value of C. In other words, the value of f_1 is fixed for a given op amp.

Let us now examine Equation (7-4) in detail. We shall deal first with the *magnitude* of the gain. At frequencies much lower than f_1, the denominator is approximately equal to one, and thus, the gain is approximately constant and equal to A_L. Therefore, the capacitor has practically no effect upon the gain at frequencies lower than f_1. At frequencies higher than f_1, the value of the denominator increases, and thus, the gain decreases. We can say that the gain of the op amp is equal to A_L *only at low frequencies* (frequencies lower than f_1). As the frequency increases above f_1, the gain drops below A_L and continues to drop as the frequency increases.

EXAMPLE 7-1

The following data are given for an op amp:

$$A_L = 1000,$$

$$f_1 = 10 \text{ kHz.}$$

Compute the magnitude of the gain at $f = 1$ kHz.

Solution

We substitute into Equation (7-4) as follows:

$$A = \frac{A_L}{\sqrt{1 + \left(\frac{f}{f_1}\right)^2}} = \frac{1000}{\sqrt{1 + \left(\frac{10^3}{10^4}\right)^2}} \simeq 1000.$$

Since the frequency (1 kHz) is much lower than f_1 (10 kHz), the gain of the op amp is approximately equal to its low-frequency value (1000).

EXAMPLE 7-2

Repeat Example 7-1 at $f = 100$ kHz.

$$A = \frac{A_L}{\sqrt{1 + \left(\frac{f}{f_1}\right)^2}} = \frac{1000}{\sqrt{1 + \left(\frac{10^5}{10^4}\right)^2}} \simeq 100.$$

Since the frequency (100 kHz) is much higher than f_1, the gain of the op amp is substantially smaller than its low-frequency value. We may now summarize:

1. The values of both A_L and f_1 are constant for a particular op amp.
2. The gain of the op amp is equal to A_L at frequencies below f_1.
3. f_1 is the frequency at which the gain begins to drop noticeably below its low-frequency value (A_L).

Now, let us examine the *phase* of the gain in Equation (7-4). Note that the phase angle is minus the angle whose tangent is (f/f_1). This means that the phase angle is also dependent upon frequency. At frequencies much lower than f_1, the tangent of the angle is approximately equal to zero. Thus, the phase angle is also approximately equal to zero. As the frequency increases, however, the absolute value of the phase angle increases. This means that there is a *finite* value of phase shift between the output voltage and the input voltage at most frequencies. The amount of phase shift increases as the frequency increases. We shall have more to say about phase shift later.

7-2   The Decibel

In frequency response analysis it becomes convenient to work with a number proportional to the *logarithm* of the gain, rather than with the gain itself. We can express the value of the gain *numerically*, as we have been doing up to this point. We can also express the value of the gain in *decibels*, as follows:

$$\text{gain in decibels} = A(\text{dB}) = 20(\log_{10} A), \qquad (7\text{-}5)$$

where: A = numerical gain,

$A(\text{dB})$ = decibel gain.

Equation (7-5) says that the decibel gain may be obtained by first taking the logarithm of the numerical gain, and then multiplying this logarithm by 20.

Since the decibel gain is always proportional to the logarithm to the base *ten*, we shall omit this designation in the future for simplicity. It is important to bear in mind that there is only *one* gain. We now have *two* ways of expressing it.

EXAMPLE 7-3

Compute the decibel gain of an op amp whose numerical gain is 10.

Solution

Substituting into Equation (7-5), we get

$$A(\text{dB}) = 20(\log A) = 20(\log 10) = 20(1) = 20 \text{ dB}.$$

We say that the decibel gain is 20 decibels, or 20 dB.

EXAMPLE 7-4

Repeat Example 7-3 for $A = 100$.

Solution

$$A(\text{dB}) = 20(\log A) = 20(\log 100) = 20(2) = 40 \text{ dB}.$$

EXAMPLE 7-5

Repeat Example 7-3 for $A = 1000$.

Solution

$$A(\text{dB}) = 20(\log A) = 20(\log 1000) = 20(3) = 60 \text{ dB}.$$

Note that each time the value of the numerical gain is *multiplied* by 10, the decibel value is *increased* by 20 dB. Remember that we can *multiply* two numbers by *adding* their logarithms.

EXAMPLE 7-6

Repeat Example 7-3 for $A = 1$.

Solution

$$A(\text{dB}) = 20(\log A) = 20(\log 1) = 20(0) = 0 \text{ dB}.$$

Let us interpret the results of this example. An op amp whose numerical gain is equal to one has an output voltage equal to its input voltage. In other words, the op amp has neither raised nor lowered the input voltage. Therefore, we say that the decibel gain is 0 dB; that is, we have neither gained nor lost decibels.

EXAMPLE 7-7

Repeat Example 7-3 for $A = 0.1$.

Solution

$$A(\text{dB}) = 20(\log A) = 20(\log 0.1) = -20(\log 10) = -20(1) = -20 \text{ dB}.$$

An op amp whose numerical gain is equal to 0.1 has an output voltage which is *smaller* than its input voltage. It is possible for this to happen at very high frequencies, as we shall see. Since the output is smaller than the input, we can say that we have "lost" voltage. In this case the minus sign indicates that we have *lost* 20 dB.

7-3   The Frequency Response Curve

We shall now apply the theory developed in the first two sections to the study of the *frequency response curve*. This curve is a plot of the magnitude of the gain versus frequency. The magnitude of the gain is plotted on the vertical axis in decibels. The frequency is plotted on a horizontal axis which has a logarithmic scale. Let us begin by examining the magnitude of the gain as given by Equation (7-4):

$$|A| = \frac{A_L}{\sqrt{1 + \left(\frac{f}{f_1}\right)^2}}. \tag{7-4}$$

Omitting the magnitude signs, we can express the decibel gain as follows:

$$A(\text{dB}) = 20 \log \left(\frac{A_L}{\sqrt{1 + \left(\frac{f}{f_1}\right)^2}}\right), \tag{7-6}$$

$$A(\text{dB}) = 20(\log A_L) - 20 \log \left[1 + \left(\frac{f}{f_1}\right)^2\right]^{1/2}. \tag{7-7}$$

We can now determine the value of the decibel gain for three different frequency ranges:

1.   At frequencies much lower than f_1
2.   At $f = f_1$
3.   At frequencies much higher than f_1

1. At frequencies much lower than f_1, we can write the following:

$$A(\text{dB}) \simeq 20(\log A_L) - 20 \log (1), \qquad (7\text{-}8)$$

$$A(\text{dB}) \simeq 20(\log A_L) = A_L(\text{dB}). \qquad (7\text{-}9)$$

Equation (7-9) says that the decibel gain is constant and equal to its low-frequency value at frequencies much lower than f_1. Refer to the frequency response curve shown in Figure 7-2. Note that the curve is a horizontal line at frequencies below f_1, indicating a constant gain.

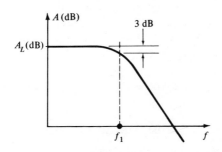

Figure 7-2

The Frequency Response Curve

2. At $f = f_1$, we can compute the value of the decibel gain as follows:

$$A(\text{dB}) = 20(\log A_L) - 20 \log (1 + 1)^{1/2}, \qquad (7\text{-}10)$$

$$A(\text{dB}) = A_L(\text{dB}) - 3 \text{ dB}. \qquad (7\text{-}11)$$

Equation (7-11) says that when the frequency of the input signal is equal to the corner frequency (f_1), the value of the decibel gain is 3 dB *less* than its low-frequency value. This can be seen by referring to Figure 7-2. We say that the gain is *down 3 dB* at the corner frequency. This is why the corner frequency is sometimes called the *3 dB frequency*.

3. At frequencies much higher than f_1, we can write the following:

$$A(\text{dB}) \simeq 20(\log A_L) - 20 \log \left[\left(\frac{f}{f_1} \right)^2 \right]^{1/2}, \qquad (7\text{-}12)$$

$$A(\text{dB}) \simeq A_L(\text{dB}) - 20 \log \left(\frac{f}{f_1} \right). \qquad (7\text{-}13)$$

Equation (7-13) says that the value of the decibel gain is equal to the difference between two terms at frequencies much higher than f_1. The value of the second term increases as the frequency increases. Thus, the value of the decibel gain decreases as the frequency increases. The descending portion of the curve of Figure 7-2 indicates that the gain decreases with increasing frequency at frequencies above f_1.

Figure 7-2 shows the entire frequency response curve. This curve indicates the value of op amp gain at different values of input signal frequency. Note that f_1 is a very important frequency. It tells us the frequency at which the gain begins to drop off noticeably from its low-frequency value. In other words, it is a kind of "warning" frequency.

We shall see shortly that it is important for us to know the *rate* at which the gain decreases in the descending portion of the curve of Figure 7-2. To do this, we shall find the *change* in the decibel gain, $\Delta A(\text{dB})$, between two frequencies, f_A and f_B. Assuming that both f_A and f_B are much larger than f_1, we can write the following:

$$\text{At } f = f_A: \quad A(\text{dB}) = A_L(\text{dB}) - 20 \log \left(\frac{f_A}{f_1} \right). \tag{7-14}$$

$$\text{At } f = f_B: \quad A(\text{dB}) = A_L(\text{dB}) - 20 \log \left(\frac{f_B}{f_1} \right). \tag{7-15}$$

If f_B is larger than f_A, we can express the change in the decibel gain as follows:

$$\Delta A(\text{dB}) = A_L(\text{dB}) - 20 \log \left(\frac{f_B}{f_1} \right) - \left[A_L(\text{dB}) - 20 \log \left(\frac{f_A}{f_1} \right) \right], \tag{7-16}$$

$$\Delta A(\text{dB}) = 20 \log \left(\frac{f_A}{f_1} \right) - 20 \log \left(\frac{f_B}{f_1} \right), \tag{7-17}$$

$$\Delta A(\text{dB}) = 20 \log \left(\frac{f_A}{f_B} \right) = -20 \log \left(\frac{f_B}{f_A} \right). \tag{7-18}$$

Suppose that f_B is ten times larger than f_A; that is, $f_B = 10 f_A$. In this case the change in decibel gain is

$$\Delta A(\text{dB}) = -20 \log \left(\frac{f_B}{f_A} \right) = -20 \log (10) = -20 \text{ dB}. \tag{7-19}$$

A ten fold increase in frequency is equivalent to an increase of one *decade*. Thus, the gain *decreases* 20 dB each time the frequency *increases* one decade. We say that the gain decreases, or *rolls off*, at the rate of -20 *dB/ decade*. Suppose now that the value of f_B is twice that of f_A; that is, $f_B = 2 f_A$. In this case, the change in decibel gain is

$$\Delta A(\text{dB}) = -20 \log \left(\frac{f_B}{f_A} \right) = -20 \log (2) = -6 \text{ dB}. \tag{7-20}$$

A twofold increase in frequency is equivalent to an increase of one *octave*. Thus, the gain decreases 6 dB each time the frequency doubles. We say that the gain rolls off at the rate of $-6\ dB/octave$. We can summarize these results as follows:

1. The gain rolls off at -20 dB/decade.
2. The gain rolls off at -6 dB/octave.

Either of these designations may be used to describe the rate of change of the decibel gain in the descending portion of the frequency response curve.

For the sake of simplicity, we shall *approximate* the frequency response curve by two straight line segments, as shown in Figure 7-3(a). Note the

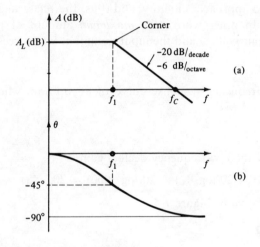

Figure 7-3

(a) Straight Line Approximation to Frequency Response Curve; (b) Phase Angle versus Frequency

resemblance to the *actual* curve in Figure 7-2. The two straight line segments intersect at a sharp *corner;* hence the name "corner" frequency for f_1. Observe that the curve crosses the horizontal axis at a frequency equal to f_C, the *crossing frequency.*

$$f_C = \text{the crossing frequency.}$$

At this frequency, the value of the decibel gain is equal to zero. This means that the output voltage is equal to the input voltage (remember that a decibel gain of 0 dB corresponds to a numerical gain of one). At frequencies higher than the crossing frequency, the value of the decibel gain is negative. This means that the output voltage is less than the input voltage (remember that a negative decibel gain corresponds to a numerical gain of less than one). As the frequency continues to increase, the value of the decibel gain becomes more negative, and thus, the numerical gain becomes even smaller. The numerical gain approaches zero as the frequency approaches infinity.

A graph of phase angle versus frequency is shown in Figure 7-3(b). It was shown in Equation (7-4) that the expression for the phase angle is given as follows:

$$\theta = -\arctan\left(\frac{f}{f_1}\right). \tag{7-4}$$

At $f = f_1$, the tangent is equal to one, and thus, the phase angle is equal to -45 degrees as shown in the figure. As the frequency approaches infinity, the tangent also approaches infinity, and thus, the phase angle approaches -90 degrees. In other words, the *maximum* amount of phase shift between the output voltage and the input voltage is 90 degrees.

EXAMPLE 7-8

Sketch the frequency response curve of an op amp whose $A_L = 3000$ and whose $f_1 = 1$ MHz.

Solution

The value of the low-frequency decibel gain is

$$A_L(\text{dB}) = 20(\log A_L) = 20(\log 3000) = 20(3.48) \simeq 70 \text{ dB}.$$

The curve is shown in Figure 7-4.

EXAMPLE 7-9

For the op amp of Example 7-8, compute the value of the decibel gain at $f = 100$ MHz.

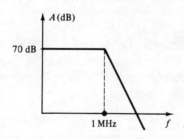

Figure 7-4

Frequency Response Curve for Example 7-8

Solution

A frequency of 100 MHz is *two decades* (100 times) above the corner frequency (1 MHz). We know that the decibel gain rolls off at the rate of -20 dB/decade. Therefore, the decibel gain at 100 MHz is 40 *dB less* than the low-frequency gain, or 30 dB (70 dB minus 40 dB equals 30 dB). We can compute the numerical value of the gain at 100 MHz by working backwards, as follows:

At $f = 100$ MHz: $A(\text{dB}) = 30 \text{ dB} = 20(\log A),$

$$1.5 \text{ dB} = \log A,$$

$$A = 31.6 \text{ at } f = 100 \text{ MHz}.$$

Note that the numerical gain at 100 MHz (31.6) is much smaller than the low-frequency gain (3000). This is because 100 MHz is much higher than the corner frequency (1 MHz).

EXAMPLE 7-10

For the op amp of Example 7-8, compute the value of the crossing frequency, f_C.

Solution

We know that the crossing frequency is generally much higher than the corner frequency. Thus, we can approximate the expression for the decibel gain by Equation (7-13).

$$A(\text{dB}) = 20(\log A_L) - 20 \log \left(\frac{f}{f_1}\right). \tag{7-13}$$

We also know that the value of the decibel gain is equal to zero at the crossing frequency. Therefore, we can substitute into Equation (7-13), setting $A(\text{dB}) = 0$ and $f = f_C$.

$$0 = 20(\log A_L) - 20 \log \left(\frac{f_C}{f_1}\right), \tag{7-21}$$

$$\log (A_L) = \log \left(\frac{f_C}{f_1}\right), \tag{7-22}$$

$$f_C = A_L f_1. \tag{7-23}$$

Substituting into Equation (7-23), we can compute the value of the crossing frequency as follows:

$$f_C = A_L f_1 = (3000)(1 \text{ MHz}) = 3000 \text{ MHz}.$$

Up to this point we have assumed that there is only *one* capacitor inside the op amp. Actually, there are quite a few capacitors present as we saw in Section 7-1. Suppose that the op amp contains *two* capacitors. Then we can rewrite Equation (7-3) as follows:

$$A = \frac{A_L}{\left(1 + j\frac{f}{f_1}\right)\left(1 + j\frac{f}{f_2}\right)}. \tag{7-24}$$

Note that there are now *two* corner frequencies, f_1 and f_2.

f_1 = the first corner frequency,

f_2 = the second corner frequency.

In general, there will be as many corner frequencies as there are capacitors. The frequency response curve appears as shown in Figure 7-5. After the

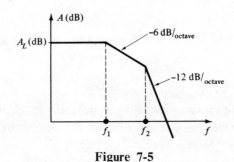

Figure 7-5

Frequency Response Curve with More Than One Corner Frequency

first corner is reached, the gain rolls off at −6 dB/octave. At $f = f_2$, the gain is already rolling off at −6 dB/octave due to f_1. There is now an *additional* −6 dB/octave roll-off due to f_2. Therefore, at frequencies above f_2, the gain rolls off at the rate of *−12 dB/octave* as shown in Figure 7-5.

The expression for the phase angle may now be written as follows:

$$\theta = -\arctan\left(\frac{f}{f_1}\right) - \arctan\left(\frac{f}{f_2}\right). \tag{7-25}$$

As the frequency approaches infinity, the phase angle approaches −180 degrees (−90 degrees for each corner). In other words, the maximum amount of phase shift between the output voltage and the input voltage is 180 degrees.

EXAMPLE 7-11

Sketch the frequency response curve of an op amp which has $A_L = 3000$, $f_1 = 1$ MHz, and $f_2 = 10$ MHz.

Solution

The curve is shown in Figure 7-6. The second corner frequency (10 MHz) is exactly one decade above the first corner frequency (1 MHz). Since the gain rolls off at the rate of -20 dB/decade after reaching the first corner, its

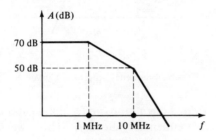

Figure 7-6

Frequency Response Curve for Example 7-11

value is equal to 50 dB (70 dB minus 20 dB) at the second corner as shown. At frequencies above the second corner, the gain rolls off at the rate of -40 dB/decade.

EXAMPLE 7-12

For the op amp of Example 7-11, compute the value of the phase angle at the second corner frequency.

Solution

Substituting into Equation (7-25), we get

$$\theta = -\arctan\left(\frac{10^7}{10^6}\right) - \arctan\left(\frac{10^7}{10^7}\right) = -129 \text{ degrees.}$$

7-4   The Significance of Frequency Response

In the first part of this chapter we discussed the nature of frequency response. We should now like to study the effect of this response upon the performance of the amplifier. We know that the general response curve appears as shown in Figure 7-7. This curve indicates that the gain begins to roll off from its low-frequency value at the first corner frequency, f_1. In other words, the value of the gain is constant only up to the first corner.

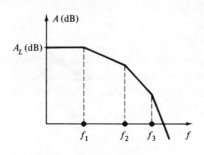

Figure 7-7

General Frequency Response Curve

If the op amp were operated open loop (no feedback), its effectiveness would decrease at sine wave frequencies above f_1. Thus, we say that f_1 is the maximum useful frequency of the op amp.

All frequencies from zero (dc) to infinity comprise a *spectrum*. A range of frequencies within the spectrum is referred to as a frequency *band*. For example, all the frequencies between f_1 and f_2 comprise one particular frequency band. The band of frequencies over which the gain is approximately constant is called the *bandwidth, BW*, or the width of the useful frequency band.

$$BW = \textbf{the bandwidth.}$$

Thus, the bandwidth of the op amp is the frequency band extending from 0 Hz (dc) to f_1, or simply f_1. Ideally, of course, we should like the bandwidth to be infinite; that is, the gain is the same at all frequencies. Due to the presence of capacitors, however, the bandwidth is always finite. Since an op amp having a large bandwidth can amplify a relatively large number of frequencies, its versatility is directly proportional to the size of its bandwidth. How do we obtain a large bandwidth? In order to have a large bandwidth, we must have a large value of f_1. This means that the values of the op amp capacitors must be very small. Thus, it is the task of the manufacturer to minimize the values of these capacitors.

The previous discussion was concerned with the amplification of sine waves. The op amp is frequently used to amplify pulse waveforms as well. Suppose that the input voltage, V_I, to an op amp is the 1 μV pulse shown in Figure 7-8(a). If the op amp is operated open loop and its gain is equal to 1000, the output voltage, V_O, will be a 1 mV pulse (1000 times 1 μV) as shown in Figure 7-8(b). The capacitors within the op amp require a finite amount of time to charge and discharge. Thus, the output voltage will not reach its final value of 1 mV immediately. The *rise time*, t_R, of a pulse is the time required for the voltage to change from 10 percent to 90 percent of its final value.

$$t_R = \text{the rise time.}$$

Therefore, due to the presence of the capacitors, the rise time of the output voltage is finite as shown in Figure 7-8(b). Note that the shape of the output waveform is somewhat different from that of the input. Thus, we can say that the output waveform is distorted.

This situation can be viewed in a different way. A mathematician named Fourier determined that every periodic waveform can be expressed as the sum of an infinite number of sine waves. This sum may be written as follows:

$$V = A_O + A_A \sin (2\pi f_A t + \theta_A) + A_B \sin (2\pi f_B t + \theta_B) + \cdots. \quad (7\text{-}26)$$

$$\underset{\text{dc}}{\uparrow} \qquad \underset{\substack{\text{1st harmonic} \\ \text{(fundamental)}}}{\uparrow} \qquad \underset{\text{2nd harmonic}}{\uparrow}$$

Each of these components represents one sine wave. A is the amplitude of the sine wave, f is the frequency, and θ is the phase angle. Frequency f_A is called the *fundamental* frequency. This is the frequency of the original periodic waveform. Frequency f_B is called the *second harmonic* frequency.

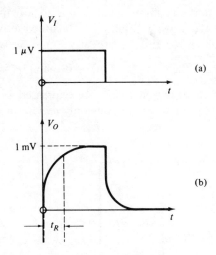

Figure 7-8

(a) Input Pulse Waveform; (b) Distorted Output Waveform

The value of the second harmonic frequency is twice that of the fundamental frequency. There is also a third harmonic component, a fourth harmonic component, and so on, up to infinity. Each periodic waveform has its own set of A's, f's, and θ's. What does all this mean? It means that every periodic waveform, regardless of shape, can be broken up into an infinite number of sinusoidal components having different values of A, f, and θ. When these components are added up, the resultant sum is the original periodic waveform. At first glance, it may seem ridiculous to split the waveform into an infinite number of components only to add them up again. This technique, however, has many useful applications as we shall now see.

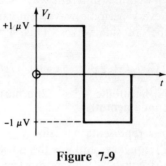

Figure 7-9

Square Wave

Let us suppose that the input voltage, V_I, to an op amp ($A = 1000$) is the $1\ \mu$V square wave shown in Figure 7-9. It can be shown mathematically that the Fourier series for this square wave may be written as follows:

$$V = 1 \sin (2\pi f_A t) + 0.33 \sin [2\pi(3f_A)t] + 0.2 \sin [2\pi(5f_A)t] + \cdots. \quad (7\text{-}27)$$

All the amplitudes in Equation (7-27) are expressed in microvolts. Note that the series for a square wave contains only *odd* harmonics; that is, there

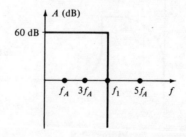

Figure 7-10

Exaggerated Frequency Response Curve

is a fundamental component, a third harmonic, a fifth harmonic, and so forth. Suppose that the frequency response curve of the op amp appears as shown in Figure 7-10. Note that the first corner frequency is higher than both the fundamental (f_A) and third harmonic ($3f_A$) frequencies, but lower than the fifth ($5f_A$) and higher harmonics. Note also that the shape of the curve has been deliberately *exaggerated*. This has been done to illustrate a point. The curve of Figure 7-10 says that the gain of the op amp is equal to 100 at frequencies below f_1, and *zero* at frequencies above f_1. Now, here is an important point. Even though all the harmonics of the square wave are present at the input, the output voltage contains only the fundamental and third harmonic components. All the higher harmonics have been eliminated by the op amp. In other words, the op amp amplifies (or passes) the fundamental and third harmonic components *only*. We say that the op amp behaves like a *filter*, passing some components and eliminating others.

The waveform of the output voltage is shown in Figure 7-11. Note that it looks somewhat like a square wave, but has a finite rise time. The waveform is distorted due to the fact that only *two* of the components have been amplified. How do we reduce the distortion? We must pass more components. This can be done only by increasing the bandwidth. Of course, if the bandwidth were infinite, all the components would pass and the output

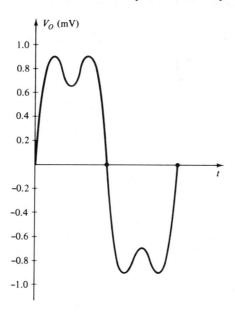

Figure 7-11

Distorted Output Waveform Containing Only First and Third Harmonics waveform would have exactly the same shape as the input. Thus, we see that an amplifier always distorts a nonsinusoidal waveform because its bandwidth is finite. As the bandwidth increases, more components pass and the output resembles the input more closely.

7-5   The Closed Loop Frequency Response

Up to this point in the chapter, we have discussed only the frequency response of the op amp alone; that is, we said nothing about feedback. Since the op amp is generally used in a feedback amplifier, we should like to know something about the closed loop frequency response. We shall see that the frequency response of a feedback amplifier has some very interesting properties. In the following discussion we shall assume that there is only one corner frequency, f_1.

We know that the gain, A, of the op amp depends only upon the op amp. On the other hand, the open loop gain, A_O, of the feedback amplifier depends upon both the op amp *and* the feedback resistors (see Chapters 4 and 5). We say that A_O is directly proportional to, but slightly smaller than A. Thus, A_O is also frequency-dependent. It has a low-frequency decibel gain, A_{OL} (dB), which is slightly smaller than A_L(dB) and a corner frequency equal to f_1, as shown in Figure 7-12. Note that the frequency response

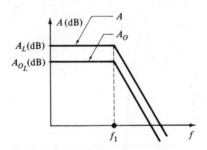

Figure 7-12

Frequency Response Curves of A and A_O

curves of A and A_O have the same general form. We shall assume, for simplicity, that the open loop gain, A_O, is approximately equal to the op amp gain, A.

In light of the previous discussion, we can write the expression for the open loop gain as follows:

$$A_O = \frac{A_{OL}}{1 + j\frac{f}{f_1}}. \qquad (7\text{-}28)$$

We also know that the expression for the closed loop gain is

$$A_F = \frac{A_O}{1 + A_O\beta}. \qquad (4\text{-}10)$$

Substituting Equation (7-28) into Equation (4-10) we get

$$A_F = \frac{\dfrac{A_{OL}}{1 + j\dfrac{f}{f_1}}}{1 + \dfrac{\beta A_{OL}}{1 + j\dfrac{f}{f_1}}} = \frac{A_{OL}}{1 + \beta A_{OL} + j\dfrac{f}{f_1}}. \qquad (7\text{-}29)$$

$$A_F = \frac{\dfrac{A_{OL}}{1 + A_{OL}\beta}}{1 + \dfrac{f}{jf_1(1 + A_{OL}\beta)}}, \qquad (7\text{-}30)$$

$$A_F = \frac{A_{FL}}{1 + j\dfrac{f}{f_{1F}}}, \qquad (7\text{-}31)$$

where: A_{FL} = **the low-frequency closed loop gain**

f_{1F} = **the closed loop corner frequency.**

A comparison of Equation (7-30) with Equation (7-31) indicates that we can equate the following terms:

$$A_{FL} = \frac{A_{OL}}{1 + A_{OL}\beta}, \qquad (7\text{-}32)$$

$$f_{1F} = f_1(1 + A_{OL}\beta). \qquad (7\text{-}33)$$

Now let us study these results in some detail. A comparison of Equation (7-31) with Equation (7-28) indicates that the expression for A_F has the same form as that of A_O. This means that A_F has both a low-frequency value, A_{FL}, and a corner frequency, f_{1F}. In other words, the value of the *closed* loop gain also decreases at the high frequencies. Equation (7-32) says that the low-frequency closed loop gain is equal to the low-frequency open loop gain divided by a factor equal to one plus the low-frequency loop gain. This is nothing more than the general feedback equation (see Chapter 4). Equation (7-33) says that the closed loop corner frequency, f_{1F}, is equal to the open loop corner frequency, f_1, *multiplied* by a factor equal to one plus the low-frequency loop gain. This means that *the bandwidth of the closed loop feedback amplifier is much larger than the bandwidth of the op amp alone*. Thus, we see now that there are *two* distinct benefits to be obtained from the incorporation of negative feedback:

1. Improved stability
2. Increased bandwidth

The frequency response curves of both A_O and A_F are shown in Figure 7-13. At frequencies below f_1, A_F is much smaller than A_O. This means that the value of the loop gain is large, which in turn indicates good stability.

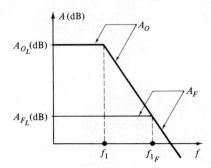

Figure 7-13

Frequency Response Curves of A_O and A_F

At frequencies above f_1, A_O begins to drop below its low-frequency value. The value of the loop gain is still large, however, meaning that the value of A_F is relatively unaffected by the change in A_O. Notice in Figure 7-13 that even though A_O rolls off at frequencies above f_1, the value of A_F remains constant. As A_O continues to decrease, the loop gain also decreases. Eventually a frequency is reached where the loop gain is no longer very large. This frequency is the closed loop corner frequency, f_{1F}. At frequencies above f_{1F}, the feedback effect disappears and the closed loop gain begins to fall below its low-frequency value. Note that the two response curves coincide at frequencies above f_{1F}. Thus, we see that like A_O, the closed loop gain has a corner frequency of its own. The value of this corner frequency, however, is much larger than the corner frequency of the op amp alone. Equation (7-32) and Equation (7-33) indicate that when negative feedback is introduced, the bandwidth is *in*creased by the same factor that the low-frequency gain is *de*creased. Therefore, we can say that the *gain-bandwidth product* of the closed loop amplifier is equal to the gain-bandwidth product of the open loop amplifier.

$$A_{FL}f_{1F} = \frac{A_{OL}}{1 + A_{OL}\beta} \times f_1(1 + A_{OL}\beta) = A_{OL}f_1. \qquad (7\text{-}34)$$

In dealing with the response curves of the open and closed loop gains, it becomes convenient to introduce a slight modification. Refer to Figure 7-14. Note that we have approximated the low-frequency closed loop gain

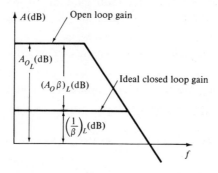

Figure 7-14

Frequency Response Curves of A_O, $1/\beta$, and $A_O\beta$

by its *ideal* value. Suppose we divide the open loop gain by the ideal closed loop gain.

$$\frac{\text{Open loop gain}}{\text{Ideal closed loop gain}} = \frac{A_O}{\dfrac{1}{\beta}} = A_O\beta = \text{Loop gain.} \qquad (7\text{-}35)$$

We know that the response curves are plots of decibel gain versus frequency. Since the decibel gain is directly proportional to the *logarithm* of the numerical gain, *dividing* A_O by $1/\beta$ is equivalent to *subtracting* $(1/\beta)(\text{dB})$ from $A_O(\text{dB})$. Thus, we can obtain the decibel value of the loop gain as follows:

$$(A_O\beta)(\text{dB}) = A_O(\text{dB}) - \left(\frac{1}{\beta}\right)(\text{dB}). \qquad (7\text{-}36)$$

Notice in Figure 7-14 that the decibel value of the low-frequency loop gain, $(A_O\beta)_L(\text{dB})$, is equal to $A_{OL}(\text{dB})$ *minus* $(1/\beta)_L(\text{dB})$. Furthermore, we can obtain the entire frequency response curve of the loop gain by subtracting the frequency response curve of the ideal closed loop gain from that of the open loop gain. We can see now why it is convenient to work with decibels. It is rather difficult to multiply or divide two curves, but it is a relatively simple matter to add or subtract them.

EXAMPLE 7-13

An op amp has $A_L = 10,000$ and $f_1 = 10$ kHz. It is used in a feedback amplifier having an ideal closed loop gain of 10. Sketch the frequency response curves of the open loop gain, the ideal closed loop gain, and the loop gain.

Solution

We shall first compute the decibel values of A_{OL} and $(1/\beta)_L$.

$$A_{OL}(\text{dB}) = 20(\log A_{OL}) = 20(\log 10,000) = 80 \text{ dB},$$

$$\left(\frac{1}{\beta}\right)_L (\text{dB}) = 20\left[\log \left(\frac{1}{\beta}\right)_L\right] = 20(\log 10) = 20 \text{ dB}.$$

Next, we compute the value of the closed loop corner frequency.

$$f_{1F} = f_1(1 + A_{OL}\beta) = 10 \text{ kHz}\left[1 + 10,000\left(\frac{1}{10}\right)\right] \simeq 10 \text{ MHz}.$$

The curves are shown in Figure 7-15. Since the frequency response curve of the loop gain may be obtained by subtracting the curve of the ideal closed loop gain from that of the open loop gain, the curve of the loop

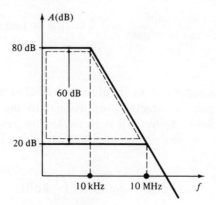

Figure 7-15

Frequency Response Curves for Example 7-13

gain is indicated by the dashed lines in Figure 7-15. The three curves are shown individually in Figure 7-16. Figure 7-16(a) shows the curve of the open loop gain. It has a low-frequency value of 80 dB and a corner frequency of 10 kHz. Figure 7-16(b) shows the curve of the ideal closed loop gain. It has a low-frequency value of 20 dB and a corner frequency of 10 MHz. Figure 7-16(c) shows the curve of the loop gain. It has a low-frequency value of 60 dB (80 dB minus 20 dB) and a corner frequency of 10

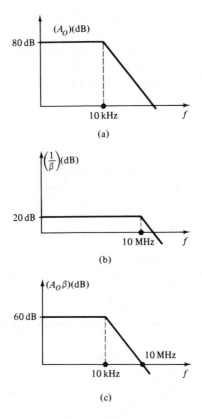

Figure 7-16

Frequency Response Curves for Example 7-13. (a) A_O; (b) $1/\beta$; (c) $A_O\beta$

kHz. Notice in Figure 7-15 that the curve of the ideal closed loop gain intersects that of the open loop gain at the closed loop corner frequency (10 MHz). At this point, the decibel value of the closed loop gain is approximately equal to that of the open loop gain, and thus, the decibel value of the loop gain is approximately equal to 0 dB, Therefore, the curve of the loop gain crosses the horizontal axis at the closed loop corner frequency as shown in Figure 7-16(c).

It was mentioned earlier that the op amp generally has more than one corner frequency. The equations derived in the previous sections should therefore be modified in order to reflect the actual situation. These equations are quite involved, however, and will not be dealt with here. Instead, we shall utilize a simple graphical technique.

EXAMPLE 7-14

An op amp has $A_L = 10,000$, $f_1 = 10$ kHz, and $f_2 = 100$ kHz. It is used in a feedback amplifier having an ideal closed loop gain of 10. Sketch the frequency response curves of the open loop gain, the ideal closed loop gain, and the loop gain.

Solution

The curve of A_O is shown in Figure 7-17(a). Note that there are two corner frequencies. The curve of the ideal closed loop gain is obtained by drawing a horizontal line at 20 dB from the vertical axis to the intersection with the

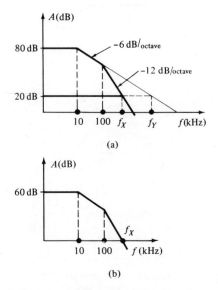

(a)

(b)

Figure 7-17

Frequency Response Curves for Example 7-14. (a) A_O and $1/\beta$; (b) $A_O\beta$

curve of A_O, as shown. Note that the closed loop corner frequency is f_X. If the op amp had only one corner frequency ($f_1 = 10$ kHz), the closed loop corner frequency would have been higher, at f_Y. Thus, we see that the presence of the second corner frequency has a detrimental effect upon the bandwidth of the closed loop feedback amplifier. The closed loop bandwidth is still much larger than the bandwidth of the op amp alone, however, since f_X is considerably higher than 10 kHz. The curve of the loop gain is shown in Figure 7-17(b).

7-6   The Slew Rate

In the previous sections we discussed the high-frequency limitation on the use of the op amp. This is essentially a "small-signal" limitation. A small signal is one whose amplitude is small in comparison with the power supply voltages. An interesting effect results when a high-frequency, large amplitude sine wave is applied to the input of a feedback amplifier.

Figure 7-18 shows a noninverting feedback amplifier. We know that the feedback voltage, V_F, develops the polarity shown. It was shown in

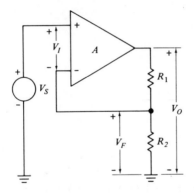

Figure 7-18

The Noninverting Feedback Amplifier

Chapter 4 that V_F automatically readjusts itself in order to keep the input difference voltage, V_I, small. Suppose that the source voltage, V_S, has both a high frequency and a large amplitude. We know that the internal capacitors require a finite amount of time to charge and discharge. Therefore, these capacitors prevent the output voltage, V_O, from responding immediately to a fast-changing (high-frequency) source voltage. In other words, we say that V_O cannot "follow" V_S, and thus, it rises very slowly. Since V_F is directly proportional to V_O, it also rises very slowly. It was shown in Chapter 4 that $V_I = V_S - V_F$. Since V_F cannot keep pace with

V_S, V_I becomes relatively large. Recall that V_I is the voltage developed across the input terminals of the op amp (see Figure 7-18).

Suppose that the last two stages of the op amp are represented as shown in Figure 7-19. The relatively large value of V_I now overdrives the first

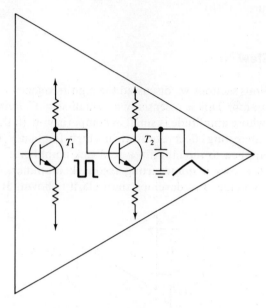

Figure 7-19

Last Two Amplifier Stages of the Op Amp

of these stages, resulting in the clipped waveform shown at the collector of T_1. Let us suppose that most of the internal capacitance of the op amp is located at the collector of T_2, as shown in the figure. The voltage at the collector of T_2 takes a finite amount of time to change because it must charge and discharge this capacitance. Therefore, the waveform at the collector of T_2, which is also the waveform of V_O, appears as shown in Figure 7-19.

Here is an important point. Although the source voltage is a sine wave, the output voltage is *not*. Thus, we can say that the output waveform is distorted. The presence of the internal capacitance limits the rate at which the output voltage can change, or *slew*. The maximum time rate of change of the output voltage is called the *slew rate*, S,

$$S = \text{the slew rate,}$$

and is specified in volts per microsecond. The slew rate of a feedback amplifier depends upon a number of factors, among them the value of the closed loop gain. Although both slew rate and bandwidth limit the maximum useful frequency of the amplifier, they produce different effects. The bandwidth is merely a limitation on the size of the gain at high frequencies. In other words, the output voltage is smaller for a given input, but it is still a *sine wave*. The slew rate, on the other hand, results in a *distortion* of the waveform.

If the output waveform distorts, the distortion can be eliminated in either of two ways. First, the *frequency* of the source can be reduced. Now, even with a large amplitude signal, the output can follow the input in order to keep V_I small, which in turn prevents the op amp stages from being overdriven. Second, the *amplitude* of the source can be reduced. Now, even though the output cannot follow the input, V_I is small enough not to overdrive the op amp stages. Thus, we see that unlike bandwidth, which depends only upon frequency, slew rate limiting depends upon both frequency *and* amplitude.

Refer to the sine wave shown in Figure 7-20. We can write the expression for this sine wave as follows:

$$V = V_P \sin (2\pi f t). \tag{7-37}$$

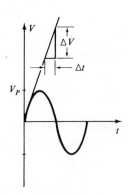

Figure 7-20

Computation of Maximum Slew Rate

The maximum time rate of change of the voltage occurs at the point at which the curves crosses the horizontal axis. This can be shown by elementary calculus to be

$$\left(\frac{\Delta V}{\Delta t}\right)_{\text{max}} = 2\pi f V_P. \tag{7-38}$$

We can now write the following expression:

$$S \geq 2\pi f V_P, \tag{7-39}$$

where: S = the slew rate in volts per microsecond (V/μs)

f = the frequency of operation in MHz

V_P = the peak value of the output sine wave in volts.

Since the slew rate is constant for a given feedback amplifier, Equation (7-39) says that the magnitude of the maximum undistorted output voltage obtainable from the amplifier is inversely proportional to the frequency of the source. As long as the value of the right-hand side of the equation is less than S, the output waveform will be sinusoidal. If either the frequency or the amplitude of V_S is increased too much, the output will distort.

EXAMPLE 7-15

A feedback amplifier has a slew rate of 10 V/μs. What is the largest undistorted output voltage which can be obtained from the amplifier at $f = 1$ MHz?

Solution

Substituting into Equation (7-39) we get

$$V_P = \frac{S}{2\pi f} = \frac{10}{2\pi(1)} = 1.6 \text{ V}.$$

This means that if the magnitude of the source voltage is increased in an attempt to obtain an output sine wave having a peak value greater than 1.6 V, the output will distort.

EXAMPLE 7-16

Repeat Example 7-15 if the frequency is reduced to 500 kHz.

Solution

$$V_P = \frac{S}{2\pi f} = \frac{10}{2\pi(0.5)} = 3.2 \text{ V}.$$

Note that with a lower frequency, we can obtain a larger sine wave at the output. Therefore, since the slew rate is constant for a given amplifier, the amplifier may be designed for either a large output voltage *or* a high frequency, but not both. Of course the larger the slew rate, the larger the output voltage which can be obtained for a given frequency.

SUMMARY

1. Due to capacitances within the op amp, the high-frequency gain decreases, and the phase angle between the input and output voltage changes with frequency.
2. The op amp gain is relatively constant at frequencies below the corner frequency, but decreases with frequency at frequencies above the corner frequency.
3. The gain may be expressed in decibel form. The decibel gain is directly proportional to the logarithm of the numerical gain.
4. The frequency response curve may be approximated by a number of straight line segments. The roll-off rate increases by 6 dB/octave each time a corner frequency is passed.
5. The finite bandwidth of the op amp limits the number of sine wave frequencies which can be amplified. It also introduces some amount of distortion into nonsinusoidal waveforms.
6. The bandwidth of the closed loop amplifier is much larger than that of the op amp alone.
7. The slew rate limits the maximum time rate of change of the output voltage. An attempt to exceed the slew rate will result in the distortion of the output waveform.

PROBLEMS

7-1.   An op amp has $A_L = 7000$ and $f_1 = 10$ kHz.
    (a) Compute the value of the magnitude of the gain at $f = 100$ Hz.
    (b) Repeat for $f = 1$ kHz.
    (c) Repeat for $f = 100$ kHz.
    (d) Repeat for $f = 1$ MHz.
7-2.   Compute the value of the decibel gain for the op amp whose numerical gain is:
    (a) 1500
    (b) 7000
    (c) 16,000
    (d) 1
    (e) 0.3
    (f) 0.02

7-3. Compute the value of the numerical gain for the op amp whose decibel gain is:
   (a) 35 dB
   (b) 100 dB
   (c) 0 dB
   (d) −5 dB
   (e) −30 dB

7-4. (a) Sketch the frequency response curve of an op amp whose $A_L = 17,000$ and whose $f_1 = 8$ kHz.
   (b) What is the value of A(dB) at $f = 800$ Hz?
   (c) What is the value of A(dB) at $f = 80$ kHz?
   (d) What is the value of the crossing frequency, f_C?

7-5. An op amp has $A_L = 22,000$, $f_1 = 7$ kHz, and $f_2 = 70$ kHz.
   (a) Sketch the frequency response curve.
   (b) Compute the value of the phase angle at f_1.
   (c) Compute the value of the phase angle at f_2.

7-6. An op amp has $A_L = 18,000$, $f_1 = 5$ kHz, $f_2 = 50$ kHz, and $f_3 = 500$ kHz.
   (a) Sketch the frequency response curve.
   (b) Compute the value of the phase angle at f_1.
   (c) Compute the value of the phase angle at f_2.
   (d) Compute the value of the phase angle at f_3.

7-7. An op amp has $A_L = 4000$ and $f_1 = 200$ kHz. It is used in an amplifier having an ideal closed loop gain of 40.
   (a) Sketch the frequency response curves of the open loop gain, the ideal closed loop gain, and the loop gain.
   (b) What is the value of the closed loop corner frequency?

7-8. Repeat Problem 7-7 for an op amp whose $A_L = 8000$.

7-9. The op amp of Problem 7-7 is used in an amplifier having an ideal closed loop gain of 80.
   (a) Repeat Problem 7-7.
   (b) Compare the results with those of Problem 7-7 and explain.

7-10. An amplifier has a slew rate of 5 V/μs. What is the largest undistorted output voltage which can be obtained from the amplifier at $f = 2$ MHz?

7-11. Repeat Problem 7-10 for $f = 5$ MHz.

7-12. An amplifier has a slew rate of 15 V/μs. It is desired that the output voltage of the amplifier be a 10 V peak sinusoid at a frequency of 2 MHz. Will the output waveform distort?

8

Oscillation and Phase Compensation

Electronics is a fascinating subject. The more you learn, the more you realize how little you know. At this point, it may seem as though we have exhausted our discussion of the op amp. There is one final problem, however. It is quite subtle, but it can destroy the usefulness of the amplifier if not taken into account. We have seen that the incorporation of negative feedback resulted in some very nice advantages, namely improved stability and increased bandwidth. Due to phase shifts within the op amp at high frequencies, however, it is possible for the feedback amplifier to *oscillate*, or generate a frequency of its own. This is highly undesirable. In this chapter, we shall study both the factors responsible for oscillations and the methods employed to prevent them.

8-1 Oscillations

A noninverting feedback amplifier is shown in Figure 8-1. Recall from Chapter 4 that the *phase* of the feedback voltage is extremely critical. For the circuit of Figure 8-1, the feedback voltage, V_F, must have the polarity shown. It is for this reason that the source voltage is applied to

179

the *plus* input of the op amp. The polarity of V_F is such as to *decrease* any change in the amplifier caused by external conditions. This is why we say that the amplifier incorporates *negative* feedback. At this point, it might be wise to reread Section 4-2 to refresh your memory.

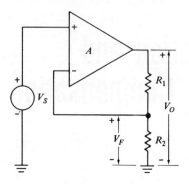

Figure 8-1

The Noninverting Feedback Amplifier

We have seen in Chapter 7 that the magnitude of the op amp gain decreases at the high frequencies. Moreover, the phase angle of the gain changes with frequency. This means that the amount of phase shift between V_O and V_I varies. If there are enough corner frequencies, it is possible for the phase to shift as much as 180 degrees at some frequency; that is, A can *reverse* its polarity.

Let us examine the situation more closely. Refer to Figure 8-2. The source, V_S, has been removed from the circuit temporarily in order to simplify the discussion. Since $V_S = 0$, we should expect to obtain no output voltage; that is, $V_I = 0$ and $V_O = 0$. Let us assume that there exists some frequency at which the magnitude of the gain is 1100 and the phase angle is 180 degrees. Assume also that $\beta = 0.001$. Suppose that the input difference voltage, V_I, in Figure 8-2, changes from 0 mV to 1 mV due to drift. Since $V_O = AV_I$, $V_O = (1100)(1\ mV) = 1100\ mV$. Due to the 180 degree phase shift, the polarity of V_O is as shown in the figure. Since $V_F = \beta V_O$, $V_F = (0.001)(1100\ mV) = 1.1\ mV$. Note that the polarity of V_F is the same as that of V_O. With the source removed, a glance at the circuit of Figure 8-2 reveals that V_I is now equal to V_F. The *original* V_I (due to drift) was 1 mV. Now, since $V_I = V_F$, the feedback has increased V_I to 1.1 mV. This *new* V_I is amplified by the op amp so that $V_O = (1100)(1.1\ mV) = 1210\ mV$. But now $V_F = (0.001)(1210\ mV) = 1.21\ mV$, and so on. Can you see what is happening? The phase of the feedback is such as to *increase* any change in the amplifier. This is known as *positive* feedback. Under these conditions the circuit "breaks into oscillation." It generates an oscillatory wave of its own at the frequency at which the op amp gain has a phase angle of 180 degrees. In other words, the circuit generates an ac output even though there is no ac input ($V_S = 0$). It may appear as though this circuit defies the law of conservation of energy. This is not the case. The circuit is supplied with dc power from the power supplies. It merely converts the dc power to ac power.

Let us examine the conditions under which the circuit will oscillate. First, the phase angle must be 180 degrees. This is necessary in order that V_O and V_F have the polarity shown in Figure 8-2. The second condition

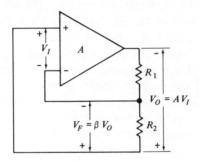

Figure 8-2

Positive Feedback

requires some thought. We saw in the preceding discussion that the presence of drift caused a change in V_I. This V_I was amplified by the op amp, reduced by the feedback network, and fed back to the input. The voltages kept increasing because the *new* V_I, which is equal to V_F, was always larger than the *old* V_I. Thus, we can say that the circuit will oscillate when V_F is larger than V_I.

$$V_F > V_I. \tag{8-1}$$

This can be rewritten as follows:

$$\beta V_O > V_I, \tag{8-2}$$

$$\beta A V_I > V_I, \tag{8-3}$$

$$\beta A > 1. \tag{8-4}$$

Equation (8-4) says that the magnitude of the loop gain must be larger than one. This is the second condition. Combining the two conditions, we can say that the circuit will oscillate if there exists a frequency at which the magnitude of the loop gain is greater than one at a phase angle of 180 degrees. We can now apply these criteria to the example of the preceding discussion. Since the magnitude of A at 180 degrees was 1100 and β was 0.001, the magnitude of the loop gain was (1100)(0.001), or 1.1. This is *greater* than one, and thus, the circuit *will* oscillate as we saw.

It should be mentioned that it is possible for the circuit to exhibit positive feedback (polarity reversal) and yet not oscillate. Suppose that the gain at 180 degrees had been 900 instead of 1100. Then the loop gain would have been (900)(0.001), or 0.9. This is *smaller* than one, indicating that the circuit will *not* oscillate. For example, suppose that V_I again changes from 0 mV to 1 mV due to drift. Then we can say that $V_O = AV_I = (900)(1 \text{ mV}) = 900$ mV, and $V_F = \beta V_O = (0.001)(900 \text{ mV}) = 0.9$ mV. Note that the new V_I (0.9 mV) is *smaller* than the old V_I (1 mV). Thus, the oscillations do not "build up," and the circuit does not oscillate.

Let us return to the more practical situation, namely the circuit of Figure 8-1. If the source voltage is applied to the circuit and the conditions for oscillation are met, the output waveform will contain *two* components. One is an output generated in response to V_S, whose frequency is the same as that of V_S. The second is an output generated by the circuit itself, whose frequency depends upon the oscillation criteria. When two waveforms having different frequencies are added, the resultant waveshape is quite different from either one. Since the frequency of the waveform generated by the circuit will generally be different from that of the source, the output waveform will have a shape which is certainly different from that of V_S. We know that an amplifier must not only increase the magnitude of the signal, but also retain the same waveshape. Therefore, it should be apparent that a circuit which breaks into oscillation ceases to be of use as an amplifier.

8-2   Stability Criteria

We saw in the last section that oscillations are to be avoided in a feedback amplifier. We also saw that some circuits will oscillate while others will not. We shall now examine the oscillation criteria in some detail to determine just when the circuit will oscillate. It was mentioned in the last section that the circuit will oscillate if there exists a frequency at which the magnitude of the loop gain is greater than one at a phase angle of 180 degrees. A rigorous analysis will show that it is the *loop gain* that must have a phase angle of 180 degrees, not the op amp gain. Therefore, it seems logical to study the behavior of the loop gain in order to determine whether or not a particular circuit will oscillate.

The loop gain is a complex number, meaning that it has both a *magnitude* and a *phase angle*. The magnitude can be obtained quite easily by subtracting the curve of the ideal closed loop gain from that of the open loop gain, as shown in Chapter 7. Since the loop gain is equal to the product of the open loop gain and the feedback factor, its phase depends upon the phase angles of both of these quantities. We have seen in previous chapters that the value of the feedback factor depends upon feedback resistors R_1 and R_2. Since there are no frequency-dependent elements (inductors or capacitors) in the feedback network, the phase angle associated with the feedback factor is 0 degrees. In other words, the feedback network containing R_1 and R_2 introduces no phase shift of its own. Therefore, we may represent the loop gain of the noninverting feedback amplifier as follows:

$$A_O\beta = \left(\frac{A_{OL}}{1 + j\frac{f}{f_1}}\right)\left(\frac{R_2}{R_1 + R_2}\right), \tag{8-5}$$

$$A_O\beta = \left[\frac{A_{OL}}{\sqrt{1 + \left(\frac{f}{f_1}\right)^2}}\bigg/{-\arctan\left(\frac{f}{f_1}\right)}\right]\left[\frac{R_2}{R_1 + R_2}\bigg/{0°}\right], \tag{8-6}$$

$$A_O\beta = \frac{A_{OL}\left(\frac{R_2}{R_1 + R_2}\right)}{\sqrt{1 + \left(\frac{f}{f_1}\right)^2}}\bigg/{-\arctan\left(\frac{f}{f_1}\right)}. \tag{8-7}$$

Equation (8-7) says that since the feedback factor has no phase angle associated with it, the phase angle and corner frequencies of the loop gain are the *same* as those of the open loop gain, which in turn are the same as those of the op amp gain. In other words, the frequency response curve of the loop gain has the same shape as that of the open loop gain. It should be mentioned that the op amp is occasionally used in applications where the feedback factor has a finite phase angle. In this case, the analysis becomes slightly more involved. However, we shall assume for the moment that the phase angle of the feedback factor is 0 degrees.

In order to determine whether or not a particular circuit will oscillate, we can use either of two techniques. We can find the magnitude of the loop gain at the frequency at which the phase angle is 180 degrees, or we can find the value of the phase angle at the frequency at which the magnitude of the loop gain is one. We shall use the second approach. When the numerical value of the loop gain is equal to one, its decibel value is 0 dB. Therefore, the magnitude of the loop gain is equal to one at the frequency at which its response curve crosses the horizontal axis. This is the crossing frequency, f_c.

Figure 8-3(a) shows the frequency response curve of the loop gain for a particular amplifier and Figure 8-3(b) shows the curve of the phase angle. Note that the curve of the loop gain crosses the horizontal axis at f_C,

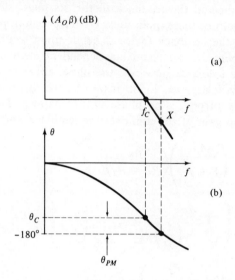

Figure 8-3

Determination of f_C, θ_C, and θ_{PM} for a Stable Amplifier

indicating that its numerical value at this point is equal to one. The phase angle at the crossing frequency is called the *crossing angle*, θ_C.

$$\theta_C = \text{the crossing angle.}$$

Note that the value of the crossing angle is *less* than -180 degrees. Since the magnitude of the loop gain decreases with increasing frequency, the decibel value is *negative* at a phase angle of -180 degrees [point X in Figure 8-3(a)]. Recall that a negative decibel gain corresponds to a numerical gain of less than one. Therefore, since the magnitude of the loop gain is *smaller* than one at -180 degrees, the circuit will *not* oscillate.

We now define a term known as the *phase margin*, θ_{PM}.

$$\theta_{PM} = \text{the phase margin.}$$

The phase margin is expressed as follows:

$$\theta_{PM} = 180 + \theta_C. \tag{8-8}$$

Assuming that $\theta_C = -150$ degrees in Figure 8-3(b), the value of the phase margin is

$$\theta_{PM} = 180 + \theta_C = 180 - 150 = +30 \text{ degrees.}$$

A *positive* phase margin is an indication of *stability* (no oscillations). The closer the phase margin comes to 0 degrees the closer the circuit comes to oscillations. Thus, we can consider the phase margin to be a kind of safety factor.

Refer now to Figure 8-4. Note that the value of the crossing angle is *greater* than − 180 degrees. It can be seen that the decibel value of the loop

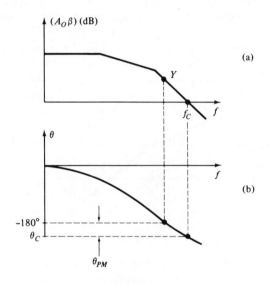

Figure 8-4

Determination of f_C, θ_C, and θ_{PM} for an Unstable Amplifier

gain is *positive* at − 180 degrees [point Y in Figure 8-4(a)], indicating that the numerical value is *greater* than one. Thus, the circuit *will* oscillate. Assuming that $\theta_C = -210$ degrees in Figure 8-4(b), the value of the phase margin is

$$\theta_{PM} = 180 + \theta_C = 180 - 210 = -30 \text{ degrees.}$$

Note that a *negative* phase margin indicates an *unstable* situation.

The preceding discussion implies a 4-step procedure to determine whether or not a particular circuit will oscillate.

1. Sketch the frequency response curve of the loop gain.
2. Determine the value of the crossing frequency, f_C.
3. Compute the value of the crossing angle, θ_C.
4. Compute the value of the phase margin, θ_{PM}.

EXAMPLE 8-1

Figure 8-5 shows the response curves of loop gain for three different feedback amplifiers, A, B, and C. The curves are drawn to scale on semilog paper. All three curves have the same three corner frequencies, 10 kHz,

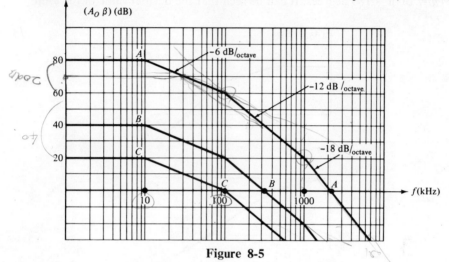

Figure 8-5

Response Curves of $A_O \beta$ for Example 8-1

100 kHz, and 1 MHz. The procedure for drawing these curves is quite simple. A horizontal line is drawn at the low-frequency value up to the first corner frequency. Then a line is drawn at a slope of -6 dB/octave (-20 dB/decade) up to the second corner frequency. Next a line is drawn at a slope of -12 dB/octave (-40 dB/decade) up to the third corner frequency, and so on. Compute the values of f_C, θ_C, and θ_{PM} for each curve.

Solution

Curve A: Curve A crosses the horizontal axis at point A in Figure 8-5. A careful reading of the curve reveals that $f_C = 2.15$ MHz. Remember that the response curves are merely approximations (see Chapter 7). However, the error introduced by these approximations is extremely small. The next step is to compute the value of the crossing angle. Since there are three corner frequencies, the expression for the phase angle may be written as follows:

$$\theta = -\arctan\left(\frac{f}{f_1}\right) - \arctan\left(\frac{f}{f_2}\right) - \arctan\left(\frac{f}{f_3}\right). \qquad (8\text{-}9)$$

To compute the crossing angle, we substitute $\theta = \theta_C$ and $f = f_C$.

$$\theta_C = -\arctan\left(\frac{f_C}{f_1}\right) - \arctan\left(\frac{f_C}{f_2}\right) - \arctan\left(\frac{f_C}{f_3}\right). \qquad (8\text{-}10)$$

The value of the crossing angle for Curve A is

$$\theta_C = -\arctan\left(\frac{2.15 \times 10^6}{10^4}\right) - \arctan\left(\frac{2.15 \times 10^6}{10^5}\right)$$

$$- \arctan\left(\frac{2.15 \times 10^6}{10^6}\right),$$

$$\theta_C \simeq -90 \text{ degrees} - 90 \text{ degrees} - 65 \text{ degrees} = -245 \text{ degrees}.$$

The value of the phase margin for Curve A is

$$\theta_{PM} = 180 + \theta_C = 180 - 245 = -65 \text{ degrees}.$$

A phase margin of -65 degrees indicates that the feedback amplifier whose loop gain is represented by Curve A will definitely break into oscillation. Note that Curve A crosses the horizontal axis at a slope of -18 dB/octave.

Curve B: Curve B crosses the horizontal axis at point B in Figure 8-5. Note that $f_C = 325$ kHz. The value of the crossing angle for Curve B is

$$\theta_C = -\arctan\left(\frac{3.25 \times 10^5}{10^4}\right) - \arctan\left(\frac{3.25 \times 10^5}{10^5}\right)$$

$$- \arctan\left(\frac{3.25 \times 10^5}{10^6}\right),$$

$$\theta_C \simeq -90 \text{ degrees} - 73 \text{ degrees} - 18 \text{ degrees} = -181 \text{ degrees}.$$

The value of the phase margin for Curve B is

$$\theta_{PM} = 180 + \theta_C = 180 - 181 = -1 \text{ degree}.$$

The feedback amplifier whose loop gain is represented by Curve B will break into oscillation. Since the phase margin is very small, however, it is quite possible that a more precise analysis will reveal that the circuit will not oscillate. We shall have more to say about this point shortly. Note that Curve B crosses the horizontal axis at a slope of -12 dB/octave.

Curve C: Curve C crosses the horizontal axis at point "C" in Figure 8-5. Note that $f_C = 100$ kHz. The value of the crossing angle for Curve C is

$$\theta_C = -\arctan\left(\frac{10^5}{10^4}\right) - \arctan\left(\frac{10^5}{10^5}\right) - \arctan\left(\frac{10^5}{10^6}\right),$$

$$\theta_C \simeq -90 \text{ degrees} - 45 \text{ degrees} - 0.6 \text{ degrees} \simeq -135 \text{ degrees}.$$

The value of the phase margin for Curve C is

$$\theta_{PM} = 180 + \theta_C = 180 - 135 = +45 \text{ degrees.}$$

The feedback amplifier whose loop gain is represented by Curve C will definitely *not* break into oscillation. Note that Curve C crosses the horizontal axis at a slope of -6 dB/octave.

We can now draw some general conclusions from the results of Example 8-1. Due to the large amount of phase shift, a loop gain whose response curve crosses the horizontal axis at a slope of -18 dB/octave is almost always indicative of unstable operation. When the curve crosses at a slope of -12 dB/octave, we say that the amplifier is *conditionally* stable. This means that some amplifiers will oscillate while others will not. A curve which crosses at a slope of -6 dB/octave is always indicative of stable operation.

We can prove that a -6 dB/ octave crossing indicates stable operation by the following reasoning: Assuming that there are three corner frequencies, the expression for the crossing angle is composed of three terms.

$$\theta_C = -\arctan\left(\frac{f_C}{f_1}\right) - \arctan\left(\frac{f_C}{f_2}\right) - \arctan\left(\frac{f_C}{f_3}\right). \qquad (8\text{-}10)$$

If the loop gain curve crosses at a slope of -6 dB/octave, f_C will be larger than f_1 and smaller than f_2, as shown in Figure 8-6. Assuming that f_C is much larger than f_1, the tangent of the angle in the first term approaches

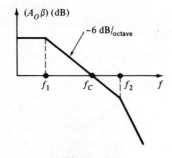

Figure 8-6

Loop Gain Curve with -6 dB/Octave Crossing

infinity, and thus, the value of the first term approaches -90 degrees. Since f_C is smaller than f_2, the tangent of the angle in the second term is smaller than one, and thus, the value of the second term is smaller than -45 degrees. We can express the second term as $-(45 - x)$, where x is the amount by which the second term is smaller than 45 degrees. Since f_3 is larger than f_2, the value of the third term is even smaller than that of the second. We can express the third term as $-(45 - x - y)$, where y is the amount by which the third term is smaller than the second. Thus, the value of the crossing angle is

$$\theta_C = -90 - (45 - x) - (45 - x - y),$$
$$\theta_C = -90 - 45 + x - 45 + x + y,$$
$$\theta_C = -180 + 2x + y.$$

The value of the phase margin is

$$\theta_{PM} = 180 + \theta_C = 180 - 180 + 2x + y = 2x + y.$$

The positive phase margin is an indication of stable operation. We can summarize the stability criteria as follows:

1. -6 dB/octave crossing: absolutely stable
2. -12 dB/octave crossing: conditionally stable
3. -18 dB/octave crossing: unstable

In other words, the greater the slope at which the curve crosses the horizontal axis, the greater the likelihood that the circuit will oscillate. This is so because each corner frequency contributes an additional component to the total phase shift, tending to make the crossing angle greater than -180 degrees.

Suppose that the three feedback amplifiers whose loop gain curves are shown in Figure 8-5 all contain an op amp whose $A_{OL}(\text{dB}) = 100$ dB. The ideal closed loop gain curves (A, B, and C) for the three amplifiers are shown in Figure 8-7. Remember that the decibel value of the ideal closed

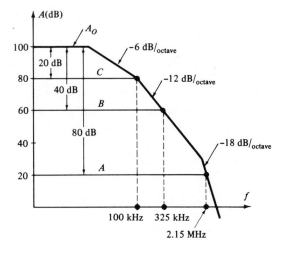

Figure 8-7

Response Curves of A_O and $1/\beta$ for Example 8-1

loop gain is equal to that of the open loop gain minus that of the loop gain. Therefore, Curve *A*, which has the *largest* loop gain (80 dB) in Figure 8-5, has the *smallest* ideal closed loop gain (20 dB) in Figure 8-7. Similarly, Curve *C* had the smallest loop gain (20 dB), and thus, has the largest ideal closed loop gain (80 dB). Recall that the closed loop corner frequency is the same as the crossing frequency of the loop gain. These frequencies (2.15 MHz, 325 kHz, and 100 kHz) are indicated in Figure 8-7 at the points where the curves of the ideal closed loop gain intersect the open loop gain curve. The preceding discussion implies that we need not sketch the loop gain curve in order to determine whether or not a circuit will oscillate. We can obtain this information directly from the open loop curve as follows:

1. Sketch the frequency response curve of the open loop gain on semilog paper.
2. Sketch the curve of the ideal closed loop gain by drawing a horizontal line to the intersection with the open loop gain curve.
3. Measure the closed loop corner frequency at the point of intersection of the two curves. This is the same as the crossing frequency of the loop gain.
4. Compute the value of the crossing angle. θ_C.
5. Compute the value of the phase margin, θ_{PM}.

EXAMPLE 8-2

An op amp has $A_L = 22{,}500$, $f_1 = 2$ kHz, $f_2 = 35$ kHz, and $f_3 = 120$ kHz. It is to be used in a feedback amplifier having an ideal closed loop gain of 1000. Will the circuit oscillate?

Solution

The decibel value of the open loop gain is

$$A_{OL}(dB) = 20(\log 22{,}500) = 20(4.35) = 87 \text{ dB}.$$

The frequency response curve of the open loop gain is shown in Figure 8-8. The decibel value of the ideal closed loop gain is $20(\log 1000) = 60$ dB. The two curves intersect at $f = 38$ kHz. This is the crossing frequency, f_C, of the loop gain. The crossing angle is

$$\theta_C = -\arctan\left(\frac{f_C}{f_1}\right) - \arctan\left(\frac{f_C}{f_2}\right) - \arctan\left(\frac{f_C}{f_3}\right),$$

$$\theta_C = -\arctan\left(\frac{38 \times 10^3}{2 \times 10^3}\right) - \arctan\left(\frac{38 \times 10^3}{35 \times 10^3}\right) - \arctan\left(\frac{38 \times 10^3}{120 \times 10^3}\right).$$

$$\theta_C = -90 \text{ degrees} - 47 \text{ degrees} - 17.5 \text{ degrees} = -154.5 \text{ degrees}.$$

The phase margin is

$$\theta_{PM} = 180 + \theta_C = 180 - 154.5 = +25.5 \text{ degrees.}$$

Thus, the circuit will *not* oscillate. Note that the closed loop bandwidth of the amplifier is 38 kHz.

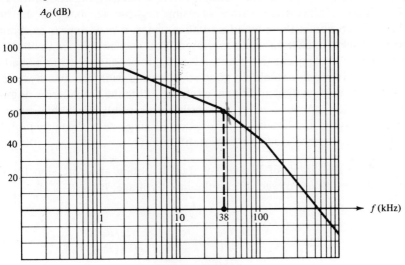

Figure 8-8

Response Curves of A_O and $1/\beta$ for Example 8-2

Refer again to Figure 8-7. Notice that as we *reduce* the ideal closed loop gain (from C to A) in order to obtain improved stability and increased bandwidth, we *increase* the loop gain. This means that the crossing frequency of the loop gain is located at points of greater slope, resulting in an increased probability of oscillation. Note that the only stable feedback amplifier in Figure 8-7 is C; that is, A and B are useless because they break into oscillation. Does this mean that we must forego good stability and wide bandwidth for fear of oscillation? The answers will be found in the following sections.

One point should be made clear before proceeding. We have used the words "stable" and "stability" to describe two different effects. When we talk about "improved stability" of the feedback amplifier, we are referring to the variation in closed loop gain due to changes in the op amp gain (see Chapters 4 and 5). Recall that this variation becomes smaller as we incorporate more and more negative feedback. When we say that a circuit is "stable" or "unstable," on the other hand, we are referring to its tendency to break into oscillation.

8-3 A Compensation Network

We saw in the last section that as we incorporate more negative feedback in an attempt to improve stability and increase bandwidth, we run the risk of oscillation. Since the purpose of using negative feedback in the first place was to obtain these wonderful advantages, it may appear as though the feedback amplifier has been overrated. You may be tempted to abandon the study of op amps at this point. Actually, the situation is not as bad as it seems. It is possible to obtain good stability and wide bandwidth without oscillations by including additional circuitry within the amplifier. A number of techniques can be used to accomplish this result. Each has its own particular assets and liabilities. Before considering one of the more popular techniques, we must study an important circuit.

Refer to the circuit of Figure 8-9. Let us obtain an expression for the ratio of the output voltage, V_O, to the input voltage, V_I.

$$\frac{V_O}{V_I} = \frac{R_Y + \dfrac{1}{j2\pi f C_Y}}{R + R_Y + \dfrac{1}{j2\pi f C_Y}} = \frac{1 + j2\pi f R_Y C_Y}{1 + j2\pi f C_Y(R + R_Y)}. \tag{8-11}$$

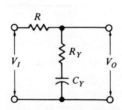

Figure 8-9

A Compensation Network

We now make the following definitions:

$$f_X = \frac{1}{2\pi C_Y(R + R_Y)}, \tag{8-12}$$

$$f_Y = \frac{1}{2\pi R_Y C_Y}. \tag{8-13}$$

We can now express the ratio as follows:

$$\frac{V_O}{V_I} = \frac{1 + j\frac{f}{f_Y}}{1 + j\frac{f}{f_X}}, \tag{8-14}$$

$$\frac{V_O}{V_I} = \frac{\sqrt{1 + \left(\frac{f}{f_Y}\right)^2}}{\sqrt{1 + \left(\frac{f}{f_X}\right)^2}} \underline{/\arctan\left(\frac{f}{f_Y}\right) - \arctan\left(\frac{f}{f_X}\right)}. \tag{8-15}$$

The decibel value of the magnitude of the ratio can be written as follows:

$$\left(\frac{V_O}{V_I}\right)(\text{dB}) = 20 \log\left[1 + \left(\frac{f}{f_Y}\right)^2\right]^{1/2} - 20 \log\left[1 + \left(\frac{f}{f_X}\right)^2\right]^{1/2}. \tag{8-16}$$

Let us examine the value of Equation (8-16) for three different frequency ranges:

1. Frequencies much lower than f_X.
2. Frequencies higher than f_X but lower than f_Y.
3. Frequencies much higher than f_Y.

1. At frequencies much lower than f_X (which are also much lower than f_Y, since f_X is smaller than f_Y), we can approximate Equation (8-16) as follows:

$$\left(\frac{V_O}{V_I}\right)(\text{dB}) \simeq 20 \log(1) - 20 \log(1) \simeq 0 \text{ dB}. \tag{8-17}$$

Equation (8-17) says that the decibel value of the ratio is equal to 0 dB at very low frequencies. This means that the numerical value of V_O/V_I is equal to one, or $V_O = V_I$. This makes sense. A glance at Figure 8-9 reveals that the reactance of C_Y is very large at low frequencies, meaning that almost all of the input voltage is dropped across the output terminals.

2. At frequencies higher than f_X but lower than f_Y, we can approximate Equation (8-16) as follows:

$$\left(\frac{V_O}{V_I}\right)(\text{dB}) \simeq 20 \log(1) - 20 \log\left(\frac{f}{f_X}\right) \simeq -20 \log\left(\frac{f}{f_X}\right). \tag{8-18}$$

Equation (8-18) says that the magnitude of the ratio rolls off at a rate of -20 dB/decade (-6 dB/octave) at frequencies between f_X and f_Y.

3. At frequencies much higher than f_Y (which are also much higher than f_X), we can approximate Equation (8-16) as follows:

$$\left(\frac{V_O}{V_I}\right)\text{(dB)} \simeq 20 \log\left(\frac{f}{f_Y}\right) - 20 \log\left(\frac{f}{f_X}\right) = 20 \log\left(\frac{f_X}{f_Y}\right), \quad (8\text{-}19)$$

$$\left(\frac{V_O}{V_I}\right)\text{(dB)} = 20 \log\left(\frac{\dfrac{1}{2\pi C_Y(R + R_Y)}}{\dfrac{1}{2\pi R_Y C_Y}}\right)$$

$$= 20 \log\left(\frac{R_Y}{R + R_Y}\right), \quad (8\text{-}20)$$

$$\left(\frac{V_O}{V_I}\right)\text{(dB)} = -20 \log\left(\frac{R + R_Y}{R_Y}\right). \quad (8\text{-}21)$$

Equation (8-21) says that the decibel value of the ratio is constant and *negative* at very high frequencies. This means that the numerical value of V_O/V_I is smaller than one, or V_O is smaller than V_I. This should come as no surprise. A glance at Figure 8-9 reveals that the reactance of C_Y is very small at high frequencies, meaning that the circuit reduces to a simple resistive voltage divider composed of R and R_Y.

The frequency response curve of the ratio is shown in Figure 8-10(a). Notice that there are two corner frequencies, f_X and f_Y. We can say that

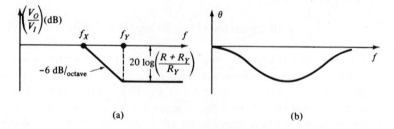

(a)   (b)

Figure 8-10

(a) Response Curve for Compensation Network; (b) Phase Angle versus Frequency for Compensation Network

C_Y acts like an *open* circuit at frequencies below f_X, and a *short* circuit at frequencies above f_Y. The curve of the phase angle is shown in Figure 8-10(b). We know from Equation (8-15) that the phase angle is expressed as follows:

$$\theta = \arctan\left(\frac{f}{f_Y}\right) - \arctan\left(\frac{f}{f_X}\right). \quad (8\text{-}22)$$

Equation (8-22) indicates that the value of the phase angle varies with frequency. The value of each term approaches 90 degrees at very high frequencies, and thus, the resultant phase angle at the high frequencies is $0°$, as shown in Figure 8-10(b). The circuit of Figure 8-9 is called a *compensating* network for reasons which will soon be apparent.

We can view the behavior of the network in another way. Let us repeat Equation (8-16).

$$\left(\frac{V_O}{V_I}\right)(\text{dB}) = 20 \log\left[1 + \left(\frac{f}{f_Y}\right)^2\right]^{1/2} - 20 \log\left[1 + \left(\frac{f}{f_X}\right)^2\right]^{1/2}. \quad (8\text{-}16)$$

Note that the expression is composed of two terms. We shall treat each of these terms separately. The *second* term is a response curve having a low-frequency value of 0 dB and a corner frequency equal to f_X. At $f = f_X$, the curve begins to roll off at the rate of -6 dB/octave as shown in Figure 8-11. The *first* term is a response curve having a low-frequency value of 0 dB and a corner frequency equal to f_Y. Note, however, that the positive sign indicates that the curve *increases* at the rate of 6 dB/octave as shown in Figure. 8-11. We can obtain the resultant curve by adding these two

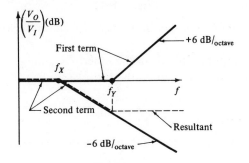

Figure 8-11

Alternate Means of Viewing Response Curve of Compensation Network

curves together. At frequencies below f_Y the decibel value of the first term is 0 dB, and thus, the resultant curve is equal to the curve of the second term alone. At frequencies above f_Y, however, the first term begins to increase at the rate of 6 dB/octave. The *positive* slope of the first term effectively *cancels* the *negative* slope of the second, resulting in a constant value of the resultant at frequencies above f_Y. Compare the resultant dashed curve of Figure 8-11 with that of Figure 8-10(a).

8-4   Phase Compensation

You may be wondering why we discussed the compensating network in the previous section. We shall see that this network is used in conjunction with the amplifier in order to prevent oscillations. Recall that oscillations result when the ideal closed loop gain curve crosses the open loop gain curve at a frequency at which the total phase shift exceeds -180 degrees. We can reduce the crossing frequency of the loop gain (thus decreasing the probability of oscillation) and still retain the same ideal closed loop gain by *reshaping* the open loop gain curve. Here is how this is done.

Figure 8-12 shows the op amp connected in *cascade* with the compensating network. Two circuits are connected in cascade when the output of one is

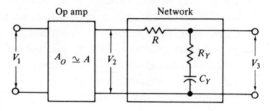

Figure 8-12

Cascade Connection of Op Amp and Compensation Network

connected to the input terminals of the other. Assuming that A_O is approximately equal to A, we can express the ratio V_2/V_1 as follows:

$$\frac{V_2}{V_1} = A_O. \tag{8-23}$$

It was shown in the last section that the gain of the compensating network, V_3/V_2, is

$$\frac{V_3}{V_2} = \frac{1 + j\dfrac{f}{f_Y}}{1 + j\dfrac{f}{f_X}}. \tag{8-24}$$

The overall gain, V_3/V_1, of two networks connected in cascade is equal to the product of the individual gains.

$$\frac{V_3}{V_1} = \left(\frac{V_2}{V_1}\right)\left(\frac{V_3}{V_2}\right) = (A_O)\left(\frac{1 + j\dfrac{f}{f_Y}}{1 + j\dfrac{f}{f_X}}\right). \tag{8-25}$$

Now, let us study Equation (8-25) in some detail. In particular, we should like to obtain the frequency response curve of the overall gain. Note that the overall gain is equal to the *product* of two terms. Therefore, we can obtain the frequency response curve by *adding* the curves of the individual terms. Figure 8-13 shows the individual curves (the curves of A_O and the

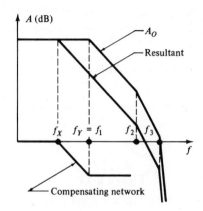

Figure 8-13

Response Curves of A_O Uncompensated, A_O Compensated, and Compensation Network

compensating network) and the resultant (the curve of the overall gain). Note that the second corner frequency, f_Y, of the compensating network has been made equal to the first corner frequency, f_1, of the op amp. Let us add the individual curves and see what happens. The presence of the first corner frequency, f_X, of the compensating network causes the resultant to begin to roll off at the rate of -6 dB/octave at $f = f_X$. At $f = f_1$, the first corner frequency of the op amp is reached. The presence of this corner might lead you to expect that the resultant will roll off at the rate of -12 dB/octave at frequencies above f_1. However, $f_1 = f_Y$ and thus, the curve of the compensating network levels off at this point, *cancelling* the effect of the first corner of the op amp. This means that instead of rolling off at the rate of -12 dB/octave, the resultant curve *continues* to roll off at the rate of -6 dB/octave until the second corner frequency, f_2, of the op amp is reached. At frequencies above f_2, the resultant rolls off at the rate of -12 dB/octave, and so on. If we consider the compensating network to be a *part* of the op amp, we can treat the cascade connection of Figure 8-12 as a single unit. Thus, we can say that the curve of the open loop gain has been *reshaped* by the addition of the compensating network.

Suppose that the *un*compensated op amp of Figure 8-14 is to be used in a feedback amplifier having the ideal closed loop gain shown. The two curves intersect at a slope of -12 dB/octave (point A in Figure 8-14),

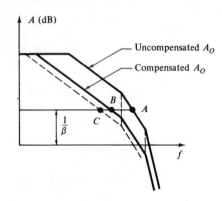

Figure 8-14

Response Curves of Uncompensated and Compensated Amplifiers

indicating possible oscillation. In other words, it is possible that the total phase shift at the crossing frequency can exceed -180 degrees. If a compensating network is added to the op amp, however, the crossing frequency is located at a slope of -6 dB/octave (point B in Figure 8-14), indicating stable operation. Of course the bandwidth is not as large as we should like it to be, but it is still much larger than that of the op amp alone.

Notice how nice this compensating network is. By selecting the appropriate values for R, R_Y, and C_Y, we can reshape the curve of the open loop gain as we please. In this way, we can insure stable operation for any value of closed loop gain.

For a given amplifier, the compensating network is generally selected to provide a specific value of phase margin. What value of phase margin shall we use? Since the phase margin is a safety factor, it would seem as though a large value is desirable. Notice in Figure 8-14, however, that the compensated curve must begin its roll-off at a lower frequency (dashed curve) in order to provide a larger phase margin. This means that the curves will intersect at point C, resulting in a smaller bandwidth. If the bandwidth is made too small, the output response to a pulse input will have a large rise time as shown in Figure 8-15(a). What happens if we make the phase margin small? First, if it is made too small, it is possible for stray wiring capacity to contribute enough phase shift to cause the circuit to break into oscillation. In other words, the safety factor might not be large enough. Second, even if the safety factor proved to be acceptable, it can be shown that the output response to a pulse input would appear as shown in Figure 8-15(b). This "ringing" on the waveform is undesirable. The waveform shown in Figure 8-15(c) has a small rise time and very little ringing, and thus, represents a reasonably good compromise. This waveform is obtained by the use of a $+45$ degree phase margin. Therefore, most feedback amplifiers are designed to have a phase margin approximately equal to $+45$ degrees.

EXAMPLE 8-3

An uncompensated op amp having $A_L = 10,000$, $f_1 = 2.5$ kHz, $f_2 = 40$ kHz, and $f_3 = 200$ kHz is to be used in a feedback amplifier having an ideal closed loop gain of 100. Sketch the response curves and determine the values of f_C, θ_C, and θ_{PM}.

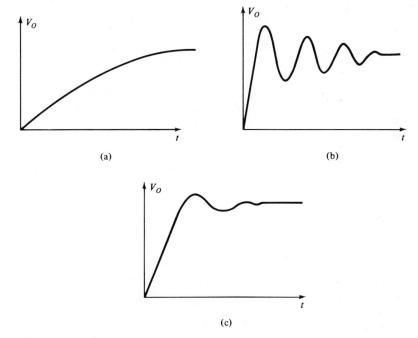

(a)

(b)

(c)

Figure 8-15

Output Voltage Response to Pulse Input for: (a) Large Phase Margin; (b) Small Phase Margin; (c) Phase Margin of $+45$ Degrees

Solution

The response curves are shown in Figure 8-16. The curve of the ideal closed loop gain (40 dB) intersects that of the uncompensated open loop gain at $f_C = 100\,\text{kHz}$ (point A in Figure 8-16). The crossing angle is

$$\theta_C = -\arctan\left(\frac{100 \times 10^3}{2.5 \times 10^3}\right) - \arctan\left(\frac{100 \times 10^3}{40 \times 10^3}\right) - \arctan\left(\frac{100 \times 10^3}{200 \times 10^3}\right),$$

$$\theta_C = -90 \text{ degrees} - 68 \text{ degrees} - 26.5 \text{ degrees} = -184.5 \text{ degrees}.$$

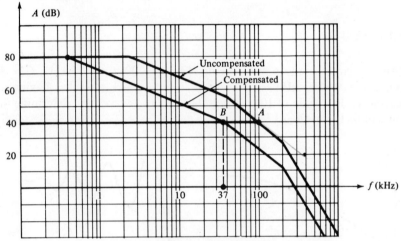

Figure 8-16

Response Curves for Examples 8-3 and 8-4

The phase margin is

$$\theta_{PM} = 180 + \theta_C = 180 - 184.5 = -4.5 \text{ degrees}.$$

Thus, the circuit will oscillate.

EXAMPLE 8-4

A compensating network is connected to the op amp of Example 8-3. It has $R = 5.6\,\text{k}\Omega$, $R_Y = 1\,\text{k}\Omega$, and $C_Y = 0.06\,\mu\text{F}$. Sketch the compensated response curve and determine the new values of f_C, θ_C, and θ_{PM}.

Solution

The value of the first corner frequency, f_X, of the compensating network is

$$f_X = \frac{1}{2\pi C_Y(R + R_Y)} = \frac{0.159}{(0.06 \times 10^{-6})(5600 + 1000)} = 400\,\text{Hz}.$$

Thus, the compensated response curve begins its roll-off at $f_X = 400$ Hz, as shown in Figure 8-16. The curve of the ideal closed loop gain intersects that of the compensated open loop gain at $f_C = 37$ kHz (point B in Figure 8-16). The crossing angle is

$$\theta_C = -\arctan\left(\frac{37 \times 10^3}{2.5 \times 10^3}\right) - \arctan\left(\frac{37 \times 10^3}{40 \times 10^3}\right) - \arctan\left(\frac{37 \times 10^3}{200 \times 10^3}\right),$$

$$\theta_C = -90 \text{ degrees} - 43 \text{ degrees} - 10.5 \text{ degrees} = -143.5 \text{ degrees}.$$

The phase margin is

$$\theta_{PM} = 180 + \theta_C = 180 - 143.5 = +36.5 \text{ degrees}.$$

Thus, the circuit will not oscillate.

8-5 A Practical Network

It was shown in the last section that the compensating network was connected in cascade with the op amp in order to prevent oscillation. In practice, however, a slightly different technique is used. Before dealing with this technique, we shall consider the following problem:

Figure 8-17(a) shows a box containing a simple voltage divider composed

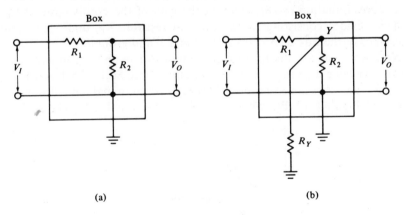

(a)   (b)

Figure 8-17

Application of Thevenin's Theorem

of resistors R_1 and R_2. If we define the gain of the box as V_O/V_I, we can write

$$A_1 = \frac{V_O}{V_I} = \frac{R_2}{R_1 + R_2}. \tag{8-26}$$

Now, suppose we run a wire from terminal Y out of the box and connect it to an *external* resistor, R_Y, as shown in Figure 8-17(b). Since R_Y is in parallel with R_2, the gain can now be written as

$$A_2 = \frac{V_O}{V_I} = \frac{\dfrac{R_Y R_2}{R_Y + R_2}}{R_1 + \dfrac{R_Y R_2}{R_Y + R_2}}. \tag{8-27}$$

Note that the connection of R_Y to the box has changed the gain. Let us compute the factor by which the gain has been changed. This can be done by dividing the new gain, A_2, by the old gain, A_1.

$$\frac{A_2}{A_1} = \frac{\dfrac{\dfrac{R_Y R_2}{R_Y + R_2}}{R_1 + \dfrac{R_Y R_2}{R_Y + R_2}}}{\dfrac{R_2}{R_1 + R_2}} = \frac{R_Y}{\dfrac{R_1 R_2}{R_1 + R_2} + R_Y}. \tag{8-28}$$

Thus, we see that the connection of external resistor R_Y has reduced the gain of the box. Note that the parallel equivalent of R_1 and R_2 is the Thevenin internal resistance of the box between terminal Y and ground Therefore, Equation (8-28) says that the gain of the box is reduced by a voltage divider consisting of the external resistor, R_Y, and the internal resistance of the box seen between terminal Y and ground.

Now what has all this to do with op amps? The op amp manufacturer makes available a *phase compensation terminal* (see Section 3-1 and Figure 3-1). R_Y and C_Y are connected between this terminal and ground, as shown in Figure 8-18. But where is R? R is the internal resistance of the op

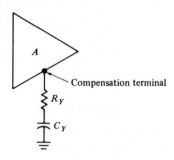

Figure 8-18

A Practical Compensating Network

amp between the compensation terminal and ground. In other words, R is a *part* of the op amp. R (an internal resistance) and R_Y and C_Y (external components) comprise a voltage divider which reduces the gain of the op amp at the low frequencies (see Figure 8-16), just as R_Y reduced the gain of the box in Figure 8-17. The values of R_Y and C_Y are selected for the desired value of f_X.

Now, let us see how a practical network is designed. Figure 8-19 shows curves of loop gain for both an uncompensated and a compensated amplifier. Note that the decibel value of the low-frequency loop gain may be written

$$(A_0\beta)_L(\text{dB}) = M(\text{dB}) + N(\text{dB}). \tag{8-29}$$

Thus, we can write

$$(A_0\beta)_L = (M)(N). \tag{8-30}$$

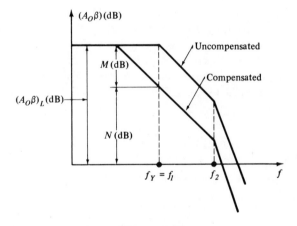

Figure 8-19

Figure for Computation of Design Criteria

M is the high-frequency attenuation of the compensating network. A glance at Equation (8-21) reveals that M may be expressed as follows:

$$M = \frac{R + R_Y}{R_Y} = 1 + \frac{R}{R_Y}. \tag{8-31}$$

R is generally much larger than R_Y in practice, so we can write

$$M \simeq \frac{R}{R_Y} \tag{8-32}$$

Assuming that A_{OL} is approximately equal to A_L, we can rewrite Equation (8-30) as follows:

$$A_L\beta = \left(\frac{R}{R_Y}\right)(N).$$

(8-33)

Solving for R_Y we get

$$R_Y = \frac{RN}{A_L\beta} = \frac{1}{\beta}\left(\frac{RN}{A_L}\right) = \frac{1}{\beta}(K)$$

(8-34)

$$\text{where } K = \frac{RN}{A_L}.$$

(8-35)

K is a constant of proportionality whose value depends entirely upon the op amp. R is the internal resistance at the compensation terminal, A_L is the low-frequency gain, and N is a quantity whose value depends upon the desired phase margin. The manufacturer generally specifies the value of K for a phase margin of $+45$ degrees. Once K is known, the appropriate value of R_Y can be computed for a given value of ideal closed loop gain. We know that the second corner frequency, f_Y, of the compensating network must be equal to the first corner frequency, f_1, of the op amp. Therefore, once the value of f_1 is known, we can compute the appropriate value of C_Y by rewriting Equation (8-13) as follows:

$$C_Y = \frac{1}{2\pi R_Y f_1}.$$

(8-36)

EXAMPLE 8-5

An op amp having $K = 20$ and $f_1 = 1$ MHz is to be used in a feedback amplifier having an ideal closed loop gain of 10. Design the compensating network.

Solution

The value of R_Y can be computed from Equation (8-34) as follows:

$$R_Y = K\left(\frac{1}{\beta}\right) = 20\,(10) = 200\ \Omega.$$

The value of C_Y can be computed from Equation (8-36) as follows:

$$C_Y = \frac{1}{2\pi R_Y f_1} = \frac{0.159}{200 \times 10^6} \simeq 800\ \text{pF}.$$

It should be mentioned that the circuit of Figure 8-18 represents only one of a number of techniques which can be used to prevent oscillations in a feedback amplifier.

SUMMARY

1.   Due to large amounts of phase shift at the high frequencies, it is possible for the feedback amplifier to break into oscillation. This destroys the usefulness of the amplifier.
2.   The amplifier will oscillate when the magnitude of the loop gain is greater than one at a phase angle of -180 degrees.
3.   The value of the phase margin is an indication of the relative stability of the circuit.
4.   The greater the slope at which the curve of the ideal closed loop gain intersects that of the open loop gain, the greater the likelihood that the circuit will oscillate.
5.   It is possible to incorporate a compensating network into the feedback amplifier to prevent oscillation.
6.   The practical op amp has a compensation terminal to which the compensating network is connected.

PROBLEMS

8-1.   A feedback amplifier has a low-frequency loop gain of 100 dB, $f_1 = 3$ kHz, $f_2 = 50$ kHz, and $f_3 = 600$ kHz.
   (a) Sketch the frequency response curve of the loop gain on semilog paper.
   (b) Determine the value of the crossing frequency.
   (c) Compute the value of the crossing angle.
   (d) Compute the value of the phase margin.
   (e) Is the amplifier stable?
   (f) At what slope does the curve cross the horizontal axis?
8-2.   Repeat Problem 8-1 for a low-frequency loop gain of 80 dB.
8-3.   Repeat Problem 8-1 for a low-frequency loop gain of 60 dB.
8-4.   Repeat Problem 8-1 for a low-frequency loop gain of 40 dB.
8-5.   Repeat Problem 8-1 for a low-frequency loop gain of 20 dB.
8-6.   An op amp has $A_L = 20,000$, $f_1 = 20$ kHz, $f_2 = 400$ kHz, and $f_3 = 4$ MHz. It is to be used in a feedback amplifier having an ideal closed loop gain of 2000.
   (a) Sketch the frequency response curves of both the open loop gain and the ideal closed loop gain on semilog paper.
   (b) Determine the value of the crossing frequency.
   (c) Compute the value of the crossing angle.
   (d) Compute the value of the phase margin.

(e) Is the amplifier stable?

(f) At what slope do the curves intersect?

8-7.   Repeat Problem 8-6 for an ideal closed loop gain of 200.

8-8.   Repeat Problem 8-6 for an ideal closed loop gain of 20.

8-9.   A compensating network has $R = 18$ kΩ, $R_Y = 1$ kΩ, and $C_Y = 0.008$ μF. Sketch the frequency response curve.

8-10.   Repeat Problem 8-9 for $C_Y = 0.0008$ μF.

8-11.   Repeat Problem 8-6 if the amplifier uses the network of Problem 8-9.

8-12.   Repeat Problem 8-7 if the amplifier uses the network of Problem 8-9.

8-13.   Repeat Problem 8-8 if the amplifier uses the network of Problem 8-9.

8-14.   A certain op amp has $K = 30$ and $f_1 = 1$ MHz. Design the compensating network if the op amp is to be used in a feedback amplifier having an ideal closed loop gain of 30.

8-15.   Repeat Problem 8-14 for an ideal closed loop gain of 50.

9

Applications

Due to its small size and large gain, the op amp finds use in many applications. It is often used in circuits which change the nature, or form of a given signal. These circuits are called *signal conditioners*. In other words, the op amp is used in circuits other than amplifiers. The op amp finds one of its most popular applications in analog computer circuitry. Analog computers perform many arithmetic and mathematical *operations;* hence the term "op" amp. In this chapter we shall discuss a number of applications of the op amp.

9-1   The ac Amplifier

Sometimes the source voltage is a complex wave, as shown in Figure 9-1. Suppose, however, that we wish to amplify only the *ac* portion of the wave. In other words, we are not interested in the dc level. We should like to arrange the amplifier circuit so that only the ac portion is amplified. What shall we do? We can place an impedance having a large value at dc and a small value at ac in series with the input. Do you know of such an impedance? Of course you do. The capacitor fills the bill perfectly. It is placed in series with the source as shown in Figure 9-2. The capacitor has infinite impedance (open circuit) at dc and, if the value of C is large, small impedance (short circuit) at ac. Therefore, the capacitor acts like a *filter*, blocking the dc and

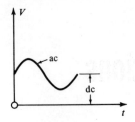

Figure 9-1

Input Waveform to Amplifier

allowing the ac to be amplified. The output voltage, V_O, in Figure 9-2 will be an amplified version of the ac component of V_S *only*.

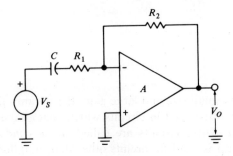

Figure 9-2

Blocking Capacitor in Input Circuit of ac Amplifier

9-2   The Approximate Equivalent Circuit

Most nonamplifier applications require that the gain be equal to the *ratio* of two impedances. One means of accomplishing this is to use the simple voltage divider circuit shown in Figure 9-3. The gain of this circuit is

$$\frac{V_O}{V_S} = \frac{Z_2}{Z_1 + Z_2}. \tag{9-1}$$

This is *not* the ratio of two impedances. If we make the value of Z_1 much larger than that of Z_2, we can write

$$\frac{V_O}{V_S} \simeq \frac{Z_2}{Z_1}. \tag{9-2}$$

Equation (9-2) says that the gain of the divider circuit is approximately equal to the ratio of two impedances if the value of Z_1 is much larger than that of Z_2. Since Z_1 is much larger than Z_2, however, the gain of the divider circuit is much smaller than one; that is, the output voltage is much smaller than the input voltage. For this reason, we prefer to avoid the use of the circuit of Figure 9-3 if at all possible. Fortunately, it is possible.

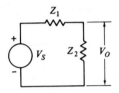

Figure 9-3

Voltage Divider

The nice thing about feedback amplifiers is that the value of the closed loop gain is dependent only upon the feedback network. The expressions for the ideal closed loop gain of the noninverting and inverting feedback amplifiers are summarized as follows:

Noninverting Amplifier   **Inverting Amplifier**

$$\frac{1}{\beta} = 1 + \frac{R_1}{R_2} \qquad\qquad \frac{1}{\beta} = -\frac{R_2}{R_1}.$$

Note that the gain of the inverting amplifier is equal to the ratio of two impedances. Note also that the value of this gain can be made greater than one. For this reason, the inverting configuration is utilized in the overwhelming majority of nonamplifier applications.

At this point it becomes convenient to obtain an approximate equivalent circuit of the inverting feedback amplifier. In order to develop this circuit, we shall make *two* assumptions:

1. The gain, A, of the op amp is infinite.
2. The input impedance, Z_I, of the op amp is infinite.

Recall from Chapter 5 that the Miller resistance, R'_2, is

$$R'_2 = \frac{R_2}{1 + A}.$$

If A is infinite, $R'_2 = 0$. Since R'_2 is across the input terminals of the op amp, as shown in Figure 9-4(a), we can say that these terminals are effectively short-circuited. In other words, $V_{I_2} = 0$. Applying Kirchhoff's voltage law to the input circuit of Figure 9-4(a), we get

$$V_S = I_1 R_1 + V_{I_2} = I_1 R_1 + 0 = I_1 R_1, \qquad (9\text{-}3)$$

$$I_1 = \frac{V_S}{R_1}. \qquad (9\text{-}4)$$

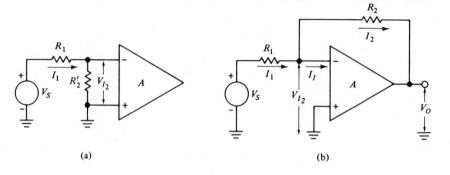

(a)　　　　　　(b)

Figure 9-4

Miller Effect

The second assumption states that Z_I is infinite. This means that the input current, I_I, to the op amp is equal to zero. Since no current actually flows into the op amp, all of I_1 flows into R_2, or $I_1 = I_2$ in Figure 9-4(b). Applying Kirchhoff's voltage law to the op amp loop, we get

$$V_{I_2} = I_2 R_2 + V_O = 0, \qquad (9\text{-}5)$$

$$V_O = -I_2 R_2 = -I_1 R_2 = -\left(\frac{V_S}{R_1}\right) R_2, \qquad (9\text{-}6)$$

$$A_F = \frac{V_O}{V_S} = -\frac{R_2}{R_1}. \qquad (9\text{-}7)$$

Equation (9-7) is nothing more than the expression for the ideal closed loop gain.

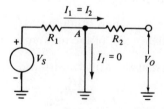

Figure 9-5

Approximate Equivalent Circuit of Inverting Feedback Amplifier

We may now represent the approximate equivalent circuit as shown in Figure 9-5. Terminal A, which represents the minus terminal of the op amp, is at ground potential. Note, however, that even though this terminal is short-circuited to ground, no current actually flows through the short ($I_I = 0$). Therefore, I_1 continues on past terminal A and flows through R_2, as shown in the figure.

9-3   The Inverter

There are times when we want a circuit that inverts the polarity of the source, but retains the same magnitude. This means that we want $A_F = -1$. This can be obtained quite simply by setting $R_1 = R_2 = R$, as shown in Figure 9-6. There is, however, one subtle problem of which you must be

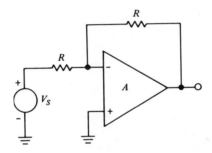

Figure 9-6

The Inverter

aware. Remember that the expression for the open loop gain of the inverting feedback amplifier is

$$A_O = \frac{AR_2}{R_1 + R_2}.$$

For most amplifier circuits, the value of R_2 is made much larger than that of R_1 in order to obtain a large value of closed loop gain, and thus, we say that A_O is approximately equal to A. For the inverter, however, $R_1 = R_2 = R$. The open loop gain is

$$A_O = \frac{AR}{R + R} = \frac{A}{2}. \tag{9-8}$$

Thus, A_O is *not* equal to A for the inverter. When drawing frequency response curves of the open loop gain for the inverter, we must be sure to divide all values of A by two.

9-4 The Adder

Analog computers use circuits which add voltages. Figure 9-7 shows the basic circuit. Three source voltages (V_A, V_B, and V_C) send three currents (I_A, I_B, and I_C) through three resistors (R_A, R_B, and R_C). Since the

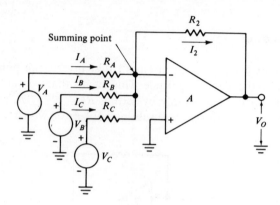

Figure 9-7

Basic Circuit for the Adder, Averager, and Scaler

summing point (minus terminal of the op amp) is at ground potential, each source voltage sees only the impedance of its own summing resistor. Thus, we can write

$$I_A = \frac{V_A}{R_A} \qquad I_B = \frac{V_B}{R_B} \qquad I_C = \frac{V_C}{R_C}. \tag{9-9}$$

We also know that no current can flow into the op amp. Therefore, all three currents must flow into R_2, and we can write

$$I_2 = I_A + I_B + I_C, \tag{9-10}$$

$$I_2 = \frac{V_A}{R_A} + \frac{V_B}{R_B} + \frac{V_C}{R_C}. \tag{9-11}$$

The output voltage can be expressed as follows:

$$V_O = -I_2 R_2 = -R_2 \left(\frac{V_A}{R_A} + \frac{V_B}{R_B} + \frac{V_C}{R_C} \right). \tag{9-12}$$

Suppose we set $R_A = R_B = R_C = R_1$:

$$V_O = -\frac{R_2}{R_1}(V_A + V_B + V_C). \tag{9-13}$$

Finally, we set $R_1 = R_2$:

$$V_O = -(V_A + V_B + V_C).\tag{9-14}$$

Thus, we see that the circuit of Figure 9-7 can be used as an *adder*. The output voltage, V_O, is minus the sum of the source voltages. If we want to get rid of the minus sign, we merely feed the output of the adder to an inverter.

9-5   The Averager

Refer again to the circuit of Figure 9-7. Suppose we set $R_A = R_B = R_C = R_1$, and $R_1 = 3R_2$. Utilizing Equation (9-13), we can express the output voltage as follows:

$$V_O = -\frac{R_2}{3R_2}(V_A + V_B + V_C) = -\tfrac{1}{3}(V_A + V_B + V_C).\tag{9-15}$$

Note that the output voltage is equal to one-third the sum of the three source voltages. In other words, the output voltage is the *average* of these voltages.

9-6   The Scaler

Refer again to the circuit of Figure 9-7. Suppose we set the values of the resistors as follows:

$$R_2 = \tfrac{1}{3}R_A \qquad R_B = \tfrac{1}{2}R_A \qquad R_C = \tfrac{1}{3}R_A.\tag{9-16}$$

Utilizing Equation (9-12), we can express the output voltage as follows:

$$V_O = -\frac{R_2}{R_A}V_A - \frac{R_2}{R_B}V_B - \frac{R_2}{R_C}V_C,\tag{9-17}$$

$$V_O = -\frac{\tfrac{1}{3}R_A}{R_A}V_A - \frac{\tfrac{1}{3}R_A}{\tfrac{1}{2}R_A}V_B - \frac{\tfrac{1}{3}R_A}{\tfrac{1}{3}R_A}V_C,\tag{9-18}$$

$$V_O = -\tfrac{1}{3}V_A - \tfrac{2}{3}V_B - V_C,\tag{9-19}$$

$$V_O = -\tfrac{1}{3}(V_A + 2V_B + 3V_C).\tag{9-20}$$

Notice in Equation (9-20) that we have *scaled* the three source voltages. In other words, in computing the average of these voltages, we have given V_B *twice* as much weight as V_A, and we have given V_C *three* times as much weight. The output voltage is considered to be a *weighted* average of the three source voltages.

9-7   The Integrator

Analog computers frequently use circuits whose output voltage is the mathematical *integral* of the source voltage. For example, if the source voltage has a dc waveform as shown in Figure 9-8(a), we should like the

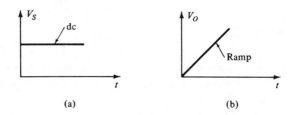

(a)   (b)

Figure 9-8

(a) Input Voltage to an Integrator; (b) Output Voltage from an Integrator

output voltage to increase linearly with time as shown in Figure 8-9(b). The waveform of Figure 9-8(b) is frequently referred to as a *ramp* function because of its resemblance to a ramp.

One way to obtain a ramp function is to charge a capacitor from a dc source, as shown in Figure 9-9(a). The waveform of the voltage across

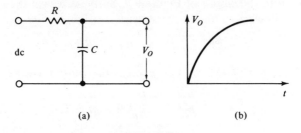

(a)   (b)

Figure 9-9

(a) *R-C* Integrator; (b) Output Voltage from *R-C* Integrator

the capacitor is shown in Figure 9-9(b). In order to obtain a true ramp, the capacitor must be charged from a *constant current source*. What does this mean? A true ramp has a constant slope. This means that the voltage increases by the same amount each second. In order for the voltage to increase linearly, the same amount of charge must be deposited on the capacitor plates each second. In other words, we want a constant flow of charge. Since current is nothing more than the rate of charge flow, a true ramp can be obtained only if the capacitor is charged by a constant current. The trouble with the circuit of Figure 9-9(a) is that as the capacitor charges up, its polarity is such as to oppose a further increase in charge. This means that the charging current begins to decrease more and more, with the result that the waveform loses its linearity as shown in Figure 9-9(b).

This problem can be solved very nicely by using the op amp integrator shown in Figure 9-10. Note that the feedback network is comprised of

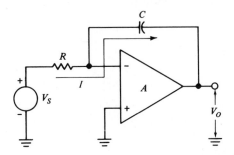

Figure 9-10

Op Amp Integrator

a resistor and a capacitor. Since the minus terminal of the op amp is at ground potential, the current, I, in the resistor is

$$I = \frac{V_S}{R}. \tag{9-21}$$

Equation (9-21) says that if V_S is a constant (dc) voltage, I is also constant. Since I also flows to C, the capacitor is charged by a constant current, resulting in a true ramp waveform at the output. It can be shown that if the positions of R and C are interchanged, the resulting circuit is a *differentiator*.

9-8 The Log Amplifier

Refer to the circuit of Figure 9-11. Note that the collector of the transistor is connected to the minus terminal of the op amp, and the base is connected to ground. Thus, we can say that $V_{CB} = 0$. It can be shown that when

$V_{CB} = 0$, the collector current, I_C, of certain transistors can be expressed as follows:

$$I_C = P\epsilon^{QV_{EB}}. \tag{9-22}$$

This can be rewritten as

$$V_{EB} = \frac{1}{Q}\left[\ln\left(\frac{I_C}{P}\right)\right]. \tag{9-23}$$

P and Q are constants whose values depend upon the transistor and the temperature. Notice in Figure 9-11 that the emitter of the transistor is connected to the output terminal of the op amp. Thus, we can say that

$$V_0 = V_{EB}. \tag{9-24}$$

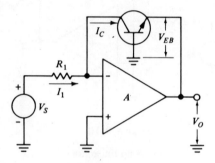

Figure 9-11

Log Amplifier

Note also that the collector current, I_C, is equal to I_1. Thus, we can write

$$I_C = I_1 = \frac{V_S}{R_1}. \tag{9-25}$$

Finally, we can express the output voltage as follows:

$$V_O = V_{EB} = \frac{1}{Q}\left[\ln\left(\frac{V_S}{R_1P}\right)\right] \tag{9-26}$$

Equation (9-26) says that the output voltage, V_O, is directly proportional to the *logarithm* of the source voltage. The log amplifier has many useful applications. For example, analog multipliers first convert the numbers to be multiplied to their logarithms, add the logarithms, and then reconvert to numerical form.

9-9   The General Problem

The general form of the inverting feedback amplifier appears as shown in Figure 9-12. The expression for the closed loop gain can be expressed as

$$\frac{V_O}{V_S} = -\frac{Z_2}{Z_1}. \tag{9-27}$$

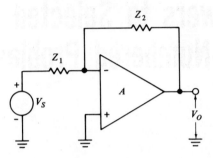

Figure 9-12

The General Circuit

In general, we can make Z_1 and Z_2 anything we please. Therefore, by selecting the proper components, we can generate a large variety of functions. It is this single factor which makes the op amp such a versatile device.

Answers to Selected Odd-Numbered Problems

CHAPTER 1

1-1. 50 kΩ, 10 kΩ, 3.33 kΩ, 1 kΩ.

1-3. (a) 3.8 V, (b) 6.2 V, (c) 2.5 mA, (d) 1.52 kΩ.

1-5. (a) 2.9 V, (b) 3.1 V, (c) 1.24 mA, (d) 2.34 kΩ.

1-7. (a) 3.2 V, (b) 6.8 V, (c) 1.7 mA, (d) 1.88 kΩ.

1-9. (a) 6 V, (b) 2V, (c) 1 mA, (d) 6 kΩ.

1-11. (a) 2 V, (b) 6 V, (c) 3 mA, (d) 0.67 kΩ.

1-13. (a) 0 V, (b) 8 V, (c) 4 mA, (d) 0 Ω.

1-15. (c) 20.

1-21. 0.185 mV.

CHAPTER 2

2-1. 2.35 V.

2-3. 2.26 V.

2-5. 3630.

CHAPTER 3

3-1. +5 V dc.

3-3. −15 V dc.

3-5.   +3 mV dc.
3-7.   +1 mV dc.
3-11. (a) +5.00225 V dc, (b) 0.045 percent.

CHAPTER 4

4-1.   (a) 833, 953, (b) 14.4 percent, (c) 5, 20, (d) 1000.
4-3.   (a) 9.98, 9.99, (b) 0.1 percent, (c) 500, 2000, (d) 10.
4-5.   −98 mV dc, −99.5 mV dc.
4-9.   (a) 5250, 10,500, (b) 618, 656, (c) 700.
4-11. 300 kΩ, 600 kΩ.
4-13. (a) 1, (b) 15 MΩ, (c) 0.014 Ω, 0.007 Ω.

CHAPTER 5

5-1.   (a) 495, 497, (b) 0.404 percent, (c) 100, 200, (d) 500.
5-3.   (a) 49.95, 49.97, (b) 0.04 percent, (c) 1000, 2000, (d) 50.
5-5.   180 degrees.
5-7.   0.05 Ω, 0.025 Ω.
5-9.   −50 mV dc.
5-11. −0.8 V dc.

CHAPTER 6

6-5.   3.75 mV.
6-7.   1.05 mV.
6-9.   (a) −10 V dc, (b) 162 mV, (c) 1.62 percent, (d) −9.938 V dc to −10.1 62 V dc.
6-11. (a) −100 mV dc, (b) 162 mV, (c) 162 percent, (d) +62 mV dc to −262 mV dc.
6-13. No.

CHAPTER 7

7-1.   (a) 7000, (b) 7000, (c) 700, (d) 70.
7-3.   (a) 56.3, (b) 100,000, (c) 1, (d) 0.562, (e) 0.0316.
7-5.   (b) −51 degrees, (c) −130 degrees.
7-7.   (b) 20 MHz.
7-9.   (a) 10 MHz.
7-11. 0.16 V.

CHAPTER 8

8-15. 1.5 kΩ, 106 pF.

References

1. *RCA Linear Integrated Circuit Fundamentals.*
2. *Handbook and Catalog of Operational Amplifiers.* Burr-Brown Research Corporation.
3. *Fairchild Semiconductor Linear Integrated Circuits Applications Handbook.*
4. *Applications Manual for Operational Amplifiers.* Philbrick/Nexus Research.
5. *Linear Integrated Circuits Systems Design Library.* Motorola Semiconductors.
6. *A Selection Handbook and Catalog Guide to Operational Amplifiers.* Analog Devices.

List of Terms

$$\left.\begin{array}{l} Z_{11} \\ Z_{12} \\ Z_{21} \\ Z_{22} \end{array}\right\}$$ Z-parameters

Z_I	Input impedance
V_I	Input voltage
I_I	Input current
A	Op amp gain
Z_O	Output impedance
V_O	Output voltage
I_O	Output current
Z_L	Load impedance
V_S	Source voltage
Z_S	Source impedance

$$\left.\begin{array}{l} V^+ \\ V^- \end{array}\right\}$$ dc power supply voltages

Z_{I_C}	Common-mode input impedance
Z_{I_D}	Differential input impedance
V_{I_1}	Voltage applied to plus input

V_{I_2}	Voltage applied to minus input
$V_S{}^+$	Positive saturation voltage
$V_S{}^-$	Negative saturation voltage
A_D	Differential voltage gain
A_C	Common-mode voltage gain
C	Common-mode rejection ratio
$\left.\begin{array}{l} R_1 \\ R_2 \end{array}\right\}$	Feedback resistors
V_F	Feedback voltage
A_F	Closed loop gain
A_O	Open loop gain
β	Feedback factor
$A_O\beta$	Loop gain
$\dfrac{1}{\beta}$	Ideal closed loop gain
Z_{I_F}	Closed loop input impedance
Z_{O_F}	Closed loop output impedance
$R_2{}'$	Miller resistance
V_{OS}	Offset voltage
$\dfrac{\Delta V_{OS}}{\Delta T}$	Voltage drift
$\left.\begin{array}{l} I_1 \\ I_2 \end{array}\right\}$	Bias currents
I_{OS}	Offset current
$\dfrac{\Delta I_{OS}}{\Delta T}$	Current drift
E	Error voltage
E_I	Error voltage referred to the input
A_L	Low-frequency gain
f_1	First corner frequency
f_2	Second corner frequency
f_c	Crossing frequency
$A(\text{dB})$	Decibel gain
θ	Phase angle
BW	Bandwidth
t_R	Rise time
A_{O_L}	Low-frequency open loop gain
A_{F_L}	Low-frequency closed loop gain
f_{1_F}	Closed loop corner frequency
$(A_O\beta)_L$	Low-frequency loop gain

$\left(\dfrac{1}{\beta}\right)_L$ Low-frequency ideal closed loop gain

S Slew rate

θ_C Crossing angle

θ_{PM} Phase margin

Index

A

ac amplifier, 207
Adder, 212
Amplifier, 16–23
Averager, 213

B

Band, 162
Bandwidth, 162
Bias, forward, 6
  reverse, 6
Black box, 31–33
Buffer, 104–109

C

Cascade, 22–23
Characteristic curve, of a diode, 5–7
  of a resistor, 1–5
Closed loop corner frequency, 167–168
Closed loop frequency response, 166–173
Common-mode rejection ratio, 57–60
Compensation network, 192–195
Control voltage, 11–12
Corner frequency, 151, 157
Crossing angle, 184
Crossing frequency, 157
Cutoff, 15

D

Decade, 156
Decibel, 152–154
Difference voltage, 49
Differential amplifier, 49, 109–112
Distortion, 21, 56, 144
Drift, 124–126

E

Error voltage, 131–134
Error voltage referred to input, 139–142

F

Feedback amplifier, 69, 82–87, 103–104
Feedback factor, 75, 100
Feedback loop, 80, 101–102
Feedback voltage, 69
Filter, 165
Frequency response, 148
Frequency response curve, 154–161
Fundamental frequency, 163

G

Gain, closed loop, 73–75, 99–100
    ideal, 75–76, 100–101
    low-frequency, 167–168
  common-mode, 58–59
  differential, 57
  loop, 75
  low-frequency, 151–152
  open loop, 75, 80–81, 100, 102–103
  overall, 23, 85–87, 104
Gain-bandwidth product, 168

H

Harmonic frequencies, 163–165

I

Input impedance, 37
  closed loop, 83, 103–104
  common-mode, 48
  differential, 48
Integrator, 214–215
Inverter, 211
Inverting amplifier, 64
Inverting input, 45

L

Load line, 7–11
Loading, 106, 109
Log amplifier, 215–216

M

Miller effect, 95–97

N

Negative feedback, 68–73
Noninverting amplifier, 62–63
Noninverting input, 45–46
Nulling, 124

O

Octave, 157
Offset current, 127–131
Offset voltage, 115–119
Offset voltage compensation, 119–124
Op amp, 23–28, 43–47
  discrete, 25–26
  hybrid, 26–27
  integrated circuit, 26
Operating point, 9–10
Operational amplifier, 23, 207
Oscillation, 179–182
Output impedance, 37–38
  closed loop, 84–85, 104
Overdriving, 21–22

P

Phase compensation, 196–201
Phase compensation terminal, 202–203
Phase margin, 184–185
Positive feedback, 72–73, 180–182

R

Rise time, 162–163
Roll off, 156

S

Saturation, 16, 52–53
Scaler, 213
Slew rate, 173–177
Spectrum, 162
Stage, 22–23
Stray capacitance, 149

T

3 dB frequency, 155
Three-terminal device, 11–16
Transducer, 105
Transistor, bipolar, 11, 32
    field effect, 11, 32

Two-port network, 33

V

Voltage follower, 87–89, 106–109
Voltage gain, 18, 37–38
Voltage transfer characteristic, 51–53,
    115–119
    ideal, 115–116

W

Worst case design, 126

Z

Z-parameters, 33–36